# SOLVENT ABUSE
## The Adolescent Epidemic?

# SOLVENT ABUSE

## THE ADOLESCENT EPIDEMIC?

JOYCE M. WATSON

CROOM HELM
London & Sydney

© 1986 Joyce M. Watson
Croom Helm Ltd, Provident House, Burrell Row,
Beckenham, Kent, BR3 1AT

Croom Helm Australia, 44-50 Waterloo Road,
North Ryde, 2113, New South Wales

Reprinted 1987

British Library Cataloguing in Publication Data

Watson, Joyce M.
    Solvent abuse: the adolescent epidemic?
    1. Solvent abuse 2. Youth — Substance use
    I. Title
    362.2′93  HV5822.S65

    ISBN 0-7099-3683-4
    ISBN 0-7099-3684-2 (Pbk)

Printed and bound in Great Britain
by Billing & Sons Limited, Worcester.

CONTENTS

List of Figures and Tables
Foreword   Professor Sir Abraham Goldberg
Preface

# FIGURES AND TABLES

## Figures

Figures and Tables

Tables

The use of 'mind-bending' drugs by man stretches
far back into history. The evolutionary triumph of
man's brain was bought in a Faustian exchange at a
price - for the anxieties and emotional perplexities
which plague him. This must represent an important
cause of his obsessive dalliance with drug abuse.
Solvent abuse is but a part of this wider problem,
and is the more pathetic because of its occurrence
in young people.

Dr Joyce Watson was first faced with this
challenge in 1972 while working as a school medical
officer in Lanarkshire and since then has acquired
unrivalled experience in this field. This book
records a dedicated procession of activities in
which she has probed into every aspect of the
subject - historical, clinical, psychological,
chemical and legal. Always within the framework of
the scientific approach she has promoted the
development of a comprehensive caring system for
the benefit of affected children involving the
school, the police, residential establishments and
various social groups, both local and national.
Every item and factor relevant to this topic has
been pursued and scrutinised; primarily the human
considerations - peer group pressure, the most
important single factor, the experimenting urge of
the teenager, the agony of the loner and young
drop-out. Each type of solvent is considered and
its dangers assessed. The susceptibility of the
tissues of the body to such solvent abuse is
considered revealing the brain, the liver and the
kidney as the most vulnerable.

Her knowledge and experience of the subject
has achieved a mature wisdom in her perspective of
solvent abuse in relation to other dangers
affecting the young. There are fewer deaths in

young people from this than from acute alcohol
poisoning. Although paternal unemployment and
single parent families may be contributing factors
in some cases, the majority of children affected
come from normal homes and in most the activity is
only transient. She has dealt with 788 solvent
abusers and has personally studied them. To all
this work has brought the attitude of the caring
doctor. Many case histories exemplify this. Each
experience and each patient has been approached in
a unique fashion in order to understand and mollify
the causative factors whatever they might be - for
example the child of twelve who takes to solvent
abuse to conjure up the image of his recently dead
mother. Legal aspects of the subject have been
dealt with in considerable detail and it is of
interest to see how the ancient common law of
Scotland has been applied successfully to this new
problem. The writing is of such quality and the
subject of such interest that many further
questions rise to mind - did the activity of the
media in 1959 blow up the article on glue sniffing
in the Denver Sunday Post into an epidemic of
solvent abuse affecting many parts of the United
States and later passing to Europe? Can the
experience in school education concerning this
problem be used for the teaching of general aspects
of drug safety within an integrated health
programme for schools, an essential survival kit
for the teenager? When the history of the social
behaviour of young people in the 20th century comes
to be written this sombre record by the author
might well constitute an important chapter.

Professor Sir Abraham Goldberg

Sir Abraham Goldberg is Regius Professor of
Medicine at the Western Infirmary Glasgow and was
Chairman of the Committee on the Safety of
Medicines 1980-86.

PREFACE

My interest in solvent abuse was first aroused in 1972 while I was employed as a school medical officer in Lanarkshire. It continued while I worked as a senior registrar in community medicine in Glasgow and subsequently as a senior research fellow in the Department of General Practice at Glasgow University.

What had begun as a quest for information about a simple problem led to an increasing involvement in the subject on a extra-curricular and purely voluntary basis. It called for both research and service components which required time and effort involving very unsocial hours.

Having worked successively as a school doctor, a medical officer to an assessment centre, a general practitioner, a university teacher and researcher and, having all along maintained my interest in community medicine, I have been well placed to study solvent abuse from a wide variety of viewpoints. This has enabled me to write a description of solvent abuse as it occurred in Strathclyde between 1970 and 1984, to place it in context against the background provided by world-wide literature and to establish contact with other researchers in Britain and beyond.

I should like to express my warmest thanks to the many children and parents who were willing to talk to me, to discuss their problems and share their experiences. Without this freely given information, this book could not have been written.

I am also sincerely grateful to the former Chief Constable of Lanarkshire, the Chief Constables of Strathclyde and their staff, without whose concern, co-operation and expertise, the entire project would have proved impossible. To Mr Kenneth Rance, the officer in charge of Calder House,

Preface

Blantyre, and his staff I should like to extend my
sincere thanks, not only for their valuable
assistance but also for their most willing
co-operation.

I would also like to express my appreciation
of the assistance rendered by the various Directors
of Education in Strathclyde Region together with
their staff and, in particular, I would sincerely
thank Mr Alistair Ramsay, Staff Tutor in Health
Education of Strathclyde Regional Council Education
Department, Glasgow Division, for his co-operation.

I am more than grateful to Strathclyde
Region's Social Work Department and the Officer/Member
Monitoring Group on Addiction for information on
the strategies devised by Strathclyde Regional
Council. In particular, I am indebted to Mr
Geoffrey Isles, Principal Addiction Officer (now
retired) as well as to Mrs Isobel Wilson, Senior
Administrative Officer and Miss June Fraser of the
Information and Resource Unit on Addiction. My
appreciation also goes to the Reporter's Office and
I should like to thank Mr Kennedy and his staff for
providing statistical information.

I should like to acknowledge with thanks the
contribution made to the study by Dr John Clarke
and the staff of the Information Services at the
Greater Glasgow Health Board as well as the unit
medical officers and staffs of the Departments of
Medical Records, all of whom provided relevant
information.

I am deeply indebted to Dr B Allam, consultant
biochemist, and his staff at Stobhill Hospital,
Glasgow and I am equally grateful to the laboratory
staff at Strathclyde Hospital, Motherwell, for
their cheerful acceptance of an increased work load
and their clearly valuable contribution by
analysing blood samples. I am especially grateful
to Dr Craig who most willingly volunteered to take
blood samples from 400 non-sniffing controls who
consented to have this done and, since the exercise
yielded very valuable information, his efforts in
making it possible are greatly appreciated.

I am especially grateful for all the advice,
encouragement and practical assistance received
from the Department of Forensic Medicine and
Science at Glasgow University. I wish to acknowledge
the contributions made to the study by the late
Professor W. Arthur Harland and by Professor Alan
Watson. I am greatly indebted to Dr John Oliver for
his development of analytical techniques for
measuring solvents in samples of blood, breath and

urine. I should like to thank very sincerely Drs
Mary King, John Stephenson and Martin Brodie for
their views on the toxicity of solvents and also
Drs Prem Misra and I. Sourindhrin for their
opinions on the long-term management of solvent
abuse. I am also pleased to acknowledge helpful
discussions held with Mr David Campbell, Social
Work Adviser (Addictions) from the Social Work
Services Group at the Scottish Office.

With gratitude, I acknowledge the co-operation,
the exchange of factual information and the
technical assistance received from the British
Adhesives and Sealants Association and, in
particular, would like to thank Mr Barrie Liss and
Mr H.E. Akerman. I would also like to express my
appreciation to Dr John Ramsey, Head of the
Toxicology Unit at St George's Hospital Medical
School, London for the additional toxicological
information put at my disposal.

I also wish to place on record my thanks to
those Members of Parliament who expressed their
concern about the problem of solvent abuse and
particularly to Messrs Harry Ewing, Jim Craigen,
David Marshall and the late James Dempsey, whose
communications over the years proved most helpful.

Legal aspects of solvent abuse have been
discussed and explained to me by the Chief Medical
Officer for Strathclyde Police and also by members
of staff at the office of the Procurator Fiscal in
Glasgow, as well as staff in the Crown Office,
Edinburgh. To all these, I express my thanks and,
in particular, to Dr W. McLay, Mr I.M. Carmichael,
Mr A.D. Vannet and Mr R.H. Dickson. I should like
to thank Detective Sergeant Wood of the Metropolitan
Police for his co-operation.

The background research to the book could not
have been completed without access to information
services and, in this context, I should like to
thank the staff of Greater Glasgow Health Board
(Library Section) and of Glasgow University Library
for the most excellent facilities extended to me.

My sincere thanks are also offered to the many
colleagues who encouraged me not only to begin my
study but to continue my researches until they
reached completion. I valued their interest and
would, in particular, thank Dr Roy Houston, Medical
Officer of Health, Lanarkshire, Dr G. Forwell,
Chief Administrative Medical Officer of Greater
Glasgow Health Board, Professor J.H. Barber of the
Department of General Practice, Glasgow University,
Dr E.T. Robinson, Woodside Health Centre and Dr

Preface

James Patterson, Medical and Dental Defence Union of Scotland. I am particularly grateful to Mr Peter Waldie and his staff of the Audio-Visual Services at Stobhill Hospital, Glasgow for the truly excellent quality of their illustrative material and I would also like to thank Mr Jim Mulhearn for his assistance with diagrams.

There are many many other colleagues and friends not named whose co-operation, interest and encouragement were positive contributions to carrying out the study and, now that it is completed, I thank them most sincerely.

Finally, I should like to place on record the great debt owed to my family for their encouragement and support over the years and, at a practical level, my mother's sharp eye for errors both of omission and commission throughout the manuscript has been of the greatest possible assistance and is therefore affectionately acknowledged. My husband, Ronald, not only provided statistical information and carried out the computing, but also put the entire manuscript on to the word processor. He managed to do this while still retaining his sense of proportion and, more important, his sense of humour, both of which have proved invaluable. I acknowledge these and indeed all his untiring efforts with great affection and a deep sense of gratitude.

The extract from The Ascent of Man by J. Bronowski has been reprinted with the permission of the British Broadcasting Corporation.

The author gratefully acknowledges generous financial assistance received from Re-Solv which made possible the publication of this book. All profits from the book will be given to Re-Solv, the Society for the Prevention of Solvent and Volatile Substance Abuse.

Chapter One

INTRODUCTION


'Butane bash is the new killer craze'
'Hooked on glue'
'How to cope with the chronic sniffer'


These are the kind of newspaper headlines which
now, in the 1980s, appear regularly. However, a
decade ago, few people had even heard of glue
sniffing and none had formed any opinions about how
to tackle the problem. For me, the introduction to
the subject occurred in 1972 shortly after moving
from a teaching hospital, where I was an
anaesthetist, to be a school doctor in Lanarkshire,
now the Lanark Division of Strathclyde Region. In
December of that year, a police superintendent gave
a talk to the school doctors on the subject of drug
abuse and, towards the end of his lecture, he made
reference to a practice which he called solvent
abuse and which he described as the deliberate
inhalation of the fumes from industrial solvents
obtained from steel-works or other industrial
premises. He specifically drew our attention to the
matter because, although it had first attracted the
notice of the police due to the anti-social
behaviour of the participants, they were genuinely
concerned about the possible health hazards
associated with the practice. The superintendent
said that it involved young people of both sexes
and that the police were particularly anxious about
it because these individuals were younger than
those who were attracted to the traditional drug
scene. The police also feared that persistent
solvent abuse would damage the physical and
emotional health of the participants. They
predicted that solvent abuse would lead to children
playing truant from school in order to indulge the

habit and that, at a future date, they would progress to the abuse of alcohol or other drugs. We were told that the attention of the police had been drawn to the matter when, in November 1970, a police patrol picked up a group of young people of both sexes, aged from 15 to 17 years, who were behaving in a drunk and disorderly fashion in the vicinity of a steel-works in an urban area. When they were questioned about their access to alcohol, the young people denied having consumed any but readily admitted that they had been sniffing the vapour from trichloroethylene which they were carrying in lemonade bottles and that this had intoxicated them. This substance had been obtained by scaling the walls of the steel-works where the trichloroethylene was kept in vats for use as a solvent and degreasing agent. They siphoned the substance from these vats into empty lemonade bottles which they had brought with them deliberately for the purpose and then climbed back over the walls. Once they were outside, they began to sniff the vapours given off with the result that they became intoxicated, began to shout and swear, staggered about and eventually attracted the attention of the police.

Other similar incidents occurred between November 1970 and April 1971, until the Chief Constable, in order to avert a possible tragedy, sent an official letter to the industrial concerns in his area alerting them to the situation and advising them to tighten up security in relation to the vats of solvents. With the access to these solvents blocked, there were no further incidents of solvent abuse for several weeks. Then, in the summer of 1971, a number of episodes occurred involving perchloroethylene, a volatile fluid used as an industrial dry-cleaner. These episodes were very similar to the previous incidents involving trichloroethylene in that the young people gained access to the dry-cleaning establishments and siphoned off the dry-cleaning agents into containers. Once outside, they proceeded to sniff the fumes and were subsequently picked up by the police as being drunk and disorderly. When interviewed, it became clear that their impairment was due to the inhaled fumes and not to alcohol. Several incidents like this occurred in different parts of Lanarkshire and caused the Chief Constable to write to the managers of the dry-cleaning establishments explaining what was happening and asking them to improve their security arrangements. Once again the access to the substance was stopped and no more incidents occurred for some time.

During the whole of 1972, few episodes involving these industrial solvents were reported, but by this time, the young people had turned their attention to finding other substances whose chemical components could be inhaled as intoxicants. One teenage girl was found unconscious in the powder room of a large department store by the manageress having been overcome by the vapours from a shoe conditioner. Several girls were found in derelict property under the influence of household dry-cleaning fluid which they had been inhaling. A ten-year-old boy was discovered, unconscious, in a school playground after sniffing a considerable amount of shoe conditioner. At the same time, garage attendants were reporting a considerable increase in the sales of bicycle repair kits to young people although cycling itself was not correspondingly more popular. Concurrently, shop-keepers were experiencing increasing sales of some cleaning materials, rubber cement and dyes together with growing thefts of these substances from open shelves.

These trends and reported incidents were monitored by the Community Involvement Branch (plain clothes, crime prevention police) who responded by establishing a liaison with local shopkeepers and chemists and by alerting them to the potentially dangerous nature of these substances when used improperly by young people. As a result, many shopkeepers removed dyes, rubber cement, shoe conditioner and dry-cleaning fluids from open shelves or restricted their sale to adults. The Community Involvement Branch also gave a series of lectures on the problem within the community, speaking to parent/teacher associations, church meetings and professional groups with a view to imparting information and encouraging co-operation.

With regard to the young people who were involved, each case which came to the attention of the police was treated informally and a visit to the home was always made by a member of the Community Involvement Branch. When it seemed to be appropriate, a referral was made to the social work department. Follow-up visits were made as a supportive measure to attempt to warn the children and their parents of the dangers of misusing volatile chemicals and also to offer them help and encouragement to abandon the practice.

As soon as the problem had been identified,

the police tried to involve other professional people in it and, by 1973, other community groups were taking an interest. The Medical Officer of Health, alarmed by the apparent growth in the number of solvent sniffers sent a letter to all medical practitioners in the area in order to disseminate information about the problem. Social work departments became involved, usually when they were notified by the school authorities that a child had been found to be sniffing volatile chemicals on school premises. The social workers were naturally concerned in such cases to find themselves responsible for children who, at best, were not fully in control of their behaviour or who, at worst, were unconscious. They were at a loss to know how to proceed and felt that they required further information about the medical and social aspects of the phenomenon. Some believed that the episodes of unconsciousness clearly indicated that solvent abuse was a medical problem while others believed that the medical aspect was only one facet of a complex situation.

The education authorities inclined to the view that far too much fuss was being made about a matter that did not apply to the school population since the young people involved were already over school age or were indulging outside school hours. They were anxious to avoid any unnecessary fuss and believed that the problem would pass.

At about this time, headlines began to appear in the local and national press such as 'Fumes charge', 'Peril to a town's children', 'Addicted to glue', 'Prisoner dies of sniffing' and - ominous note - 'Solvent sniffing is on the increase'. Initially, there seemed to be no logical basis for this panic in the community. Solvent abuse was a new phenomenon and there was little information available about the toxicity of these substances when abused, about the reasons for their abuse or about the young people who participated in the practice. It seemed to me that the press and some professional groups were stating the existence of a problem without defining it properly or describing its extent. Did it represent a relatively small problem which had been given too much importance by virtue of its handling by the press and some community groups or was it the tip of the proverbial iceberg?

By October 1973, informal meetings were taking place involving interested and concerned professional people from community health, education, social work and the police. It was suggested that legislation might have to be introduced to limit or prevent the sale of all offending agents although these were still unnamed and undefined. Other proposals included the involvement of the manufacturers so that the more toxic substances present in some products could be replaced by less noxious chemicals. It was proposed that the police might be able to persuade shopkeepers and garage owners to be vigilant about the sale of products with intoxicating vapours to schoolchildren and some stores were prevailed upon to remove all articles of this type from open shelves and to refuse to sell them to young people. As an educational measure, there was discussion of a campaign of health education about the hazards of solvent abuse which was to be directed at schoolchildren.

At this point, I became convinced that there was a need for a detailed investigation of the problem. Fortunately, in October 1973, I was back at Glasgow University for one academic year to study for the postgraduate Diploma of Public Health. As part of this course it is necessary to submit a thesis on some relevant and preferably topical subject. Solvent abuse immediately came to mind as a suitable topic for such a thesis and this was the start of my active interest in the subject.

Initially, I set out to describe this apparently new phenomenon which had appeared in Lanarkshire. For this, I had to describe the substances involved, identify the relevant chemicals that they contained and determine the age, sex and any other salient characteristics of those who were involved in their abuse. I also had to identify the range of effects which were obtained with particular emphasis on possibly harmful effects. During my year of research at Glasgow University, I was able to interview many people in different professions about the matter and obtained much current information about the extent and characteristics of the practice. At the same time, I was able to search the world literature on the subject.

I discovered that solvent abuse was not a new phenomenon but that the abuse of chemicals by inhaling their vapours is as old as history. Much nearer to our own time and culture, it appeared that this deliberate abuse of chemicals by young people had been a problem involving petrol in the 1950s and adhesives in the 1960s. This had occurred mainly in America and correspondence with researchers there was depressing since it revealed that solvent abuse had almost vanished from the North American adolescent scene but only, it was thought, because it had been replaced by the abuse of street drugs which were cheap and readily available.

The project within Lanarkshire was not without difficulty. Since only the police authorities had collected statistical information on the subject, a study of their data was undertaken. This indicated that solvent abuse was mainly a group activity involving children and young people aged between 9 and 17 years most of whom lived in urban areas. Most of the participants were male and some had been involved in anti-social activities. This was useful but it was far from complete or conclusive since there was no information about individuals who might be quietly involved in solvent abuse at home.

An attempt was made to conduct a prevalence survey in selected Lanarkshire schools. It was hoped that this would help to determine the extent to which solvent abuse involved children between the ages of 13 and 15. The preparatory work was almost completed and permission for the survey had been obtained from the Director of Education when details of the project were leaked to the press by some unknown person. The resulting unwanted publicity caused the abandonment of the project. This was my first lesson about the difficulties of working in an area which is politically and emotionally sensitive.

In order to replace this survey and to complete my thesis, I interviewed a number of people drawn from different groups such as school doctors and nurses, social workers, police, teachers and parents and asked them for their opinion on solvent abuse. Some social workers considered solvent abuse as being entirely a medical problem although others disagreed. Some doctors and nurses thought that the sniffers were initially a medical matter but that they should then be passed on to the social workers. Teachers felt that the problem was mainly medical. All professional groups thought that the problem should be tackled by using 'a team including ourselves'. All but one of the six parents interviewed thought that the matter should be dealt with by others and that they should not be personally involved.

By June 1974, the project had been completed. Although some information had been collected about solvent abuse, it was clear that much more was required before decisions about the matter could be made on a rational basis.

One thing that did become clear was that, although the practice was originally called 'solvent abuse' by the police because of the industrial solvents used in the first cases encountered by them, this term was seen to be inaccurate in the light of evidence that other chemicals were also abused. Other terms used to label the practice have been 'glue sniffing', 'hydrocarbon sniffing' and 'volatile substance abuse' but all of these are inaccurate because they fail to cover the whole spectrum of substances that can be abused by inhalation. The most accurate and general term that is in current use is probably 'inhalant misuse'. However, the name used for the practice is relatively unimportant in comparison with a clear understanding of the activity itself. This is described in Chapters 2 and 3.

After completion of this first project in 1974, I continued my research interest in solvent abuse and kept in touch with others in various professional groups who continued to monitor the situation. By the end of 1975, several hundred young people were known to have abused a wide variety of volatile chemicals which ranged from industrial solvents to shoe-cleaner and dry-cleaning fluids and latterly to adhesives.

The practice itself came to light in a variety of ways. The resulting disruptive behaviour or thefts often drew the attention of the police. Sometimes, social workers interviewing children because of various other problems came upon solvent abuse inadvertently. The staff of Lanarkshire's assessment centre also discovered it when dealing with the case-work of children, most of whom had been admitted for a wide range of problems. None of the children discovered by these agencies died or had to be admitted to hospital due to solvent abuse. However, other children who were not known to these agencies had been hospitalised because of solvent abuse in the period from 1970 to 1975. In addition two had died, one in 1970 and the other in 1975. At that point, the picture was very confusing. What did it mean?

In 1976, the first working party in Scotland was set up in Lanarkshire on a multi-disciplinary basis. Its members were drawn from health, education, social work, the police, the Reporter's office, educational psychology and the child guidance service. Regular meetings were arranged

7

and the essential roles of the group were considered to be the establishment of in-service training for the various professional bodies that might encounter the problem and the free exchange of information and opinions about the matter. One of the first tasks was to prepare a pamphlet on solvent abuse which was intended to disseminate factual information to people involved in dealing with the problem. This pamphlet reflected current knowledge of solvent abuse and was intended to be updated as more information became available.

In 1976, in nearby Glasgow, various professional groups began to have fears similar to those expressed in Lanarkshire. Until then, it had seemed that the problem was confined to the industrial belt of Lanarkshire but it became clear that this was no longer the case. Therefore, using the earlier experience gained in Lanarkshire, it was decided that early positive measures should be adopted rather than a 'wait and see' approach.

In June of that year, a working party was set up by the District Medical Officer in the East End of Glasgow. This is an area of urban deprivation which was then, and still is, undergoing redevelopment. This working party consisted of representatives from teaching, the School Health Service, educational psychology, psychiatry, the Reporter's office, the Social Work Department and the police. In August a pamphlet was issued to disseminate current information about the problem of solvent abuse and also to provide useful names and addresses as contacts for the referral of cases or other problems. Regular meetings of the group took place to facilitate the exchange of information and to enable those who worked in one speciality to see the problem from other standpoints. As a result, referrals could and did take place between specialities.

In spite of this early response to the first expressions of disquiet about solvent abuse in Glasgow, two deaths occurred during 1976, one being a schoolboy of 15 in the east end and the other a boy of 16 from the north of the city. Following this, there was an increased demand for more information about solvent abuse from all sectors of the population in Strathclyde. These included professional groups, local councillors and Members of Parliament and all wanted to know about the practice of solvent abuse, its participants, the associated problems and the effects, particularly the toxic effects.

From about the same time, there has been an increasing demand for the same information from all over Britain and this book is an attempt to answer these questions and others which have been posed over the years about solvent abuse. In this book, I give a description of what happened in the Lanark and Glasgow Districts of Strathclyde in the belief tha'. the experience and information gained there is also valid in other parts of Britain. It contains the results of the research and field work of many people and I have tried to present it as completely and comprehensively as possible. The book has been written because, since 1973, throughout my work in this field, I have been aware of the strong feelings about solvent abuse held by many people from all walks of life. In particular, I have noted a great deal of anxiety and fear. In any situation which provokes fear, I believe that the first response should be to find out all the available facts and to interpret them in a way that gives the widest perspective to the matter.

This is a book about solvent abuse. It is also a book about people. One of its premises is that effective prevention or treatment of any problem must ultimately depend on knowledge and understanding. This book has been written to increase the understanding of solvent abuse. It will be of interest to those who are directly involved in dealing with solvent abusers, to those involved in providing services for children or simply to those who feel that they should know more about the problem. The statements made in it are not intended to give a do-it-yourself guide to the solution of the solvent abuse problem. Instead, it describes how the problem arose in one area, the resulting problems and the various strategies that were developed to deal with it at a local level and beyond. Obviously, not all the events described will occur elsewhere and even if they did, the circumstances and available resources might be quite different. However, it is hoped that people in other parts of Britain may find it useful.

I have attempted not to moralise or criticise but instead to find the facts and to interpret their meaning and implications for the individuals who abuse solvents, their families, their friends and the community in which they live.

The next chapter describes the history of inhalant misuse in order to give a proper historical perspective to the present situation. It points out that man has always experimented with

mind-altering substances and that many were used
because of their effects on mood or behaviour
before other qualities, such as pain relief or
anaesthesia were exploited.

Chapter 3 describes the practice of solvent
abuse among the young people in Strathclyde.
Details are given about the wide variety of
substances that were abused together with information
about the various methods of abuse. It describes
the mainly group nature of the activity, the wide
range of places chosen by the young people for it
and the individual variation in the degree and
duration of involvement. The clustering of cases in
specific schools and in specific areas is discussed
and also the transient nature of the activity,
coming and going as it does from time to time.

The participants are described in detail in
Chapter 4. Information is given about their
age-range and sex along with details of other
factors such as social circumstances and residence
in urban or rural areas. It is shown that solvent
abuse by young people occurs in all parts of our
society and not just among certain groups. The
collection of information on prevalence is
discussed in Chapter 5.

Chapter 6 deals in great detail with the
consequences of inhaling volatile chemicals for
intoxication. The range of effects is divided into
the immediate effects associated with acute
episodes of intoxication and those seen between
episodes on a long-term basis. The difficulties of
assessing toxic effects are described and so are
the factors associated with deaths.

The impact of solvent abuse on a family
situation is described in Chapter 7. Some of the
information was obtained during confidential
contacts with the parents of solvent abusers and
some was noted during home visits by the author and
others.

The community aspects of solvent abuse are
discussed in Chapter 8. It is clear that the
problem presents in many ways to many different
professional groups. As a result, the strategies
developed in Strathclyde, like the many factors in
the problem, have been many and varied. Some
strategies have started with only one group, such
as the police, being involved and have ended as a
corporate approach with all of the community
agencies participating. Each method for tackling
the problem has also had to be adapted locally to
satisfy local needs.

Introduction

Chapter 9 discusses in detail the wider implications of dealing with solvent abuse beyond the community level. These involve the actions taken by the manufacturers, by politicians, by Parliament and by the legal system.

The conclusions about solvent abuse in Strathclyde are presented in Chapter 10. When it was first observed in November 1970, it appeared to be new, different and simple but the years of research and service experience in Strathclyde have shown it to be complicated and old. It is complicated in its various forms of presentation, its causes, its management and its possible solutions. One of the difficulties is that its complexity means that not all statements will fit all individuals in all circumstances. It is old because, on closer scrutiny, it would seem to be a new manifestation of an old phenomenon.

Chapter Two

THE HISTORY OF SUBSTANCE ABUSE

In the first chapter of his book <u>The Ascent of Man</u>,
Dr Bronowski has this to say when comparing man
with a fish such as the grunion.

> Nature - that is biological evolution - has
> not fitted man to any specific environment. On
> the contrary, he has a rather crude survival
> kit; and yet - this is the paradox of the
> human condition - one that fits him to all
> environments. Among the multitude of animals
> which scamper, fly, burrow and swim around us,
> man is the only one who is not locked into his
> environment. His imagination, his reason, his
> emotional subtlety and toughness make it
> possible for him not to accept the environment
> but to change it.

This capacity to change his environment, which man
possesses, has on occasions led him to alter his
surroundings physically and at others to move off
to a more acceptable location. However, another way
of changing the environment is for man to alter his
own mental state thereby changing his perception of
it. About 30 years ago in an address to the New
York Academy of Sciences, Aldous Huxley said that
pharmacology was older than agriculture. He
explained that each twig, root, grain and berry had
been exploited for all its possible uses, not just
to satiate the pangs of hunger and thirst but also
to satisfy man's need to alter his state of
consciousness.
    During the last two decades, anthropologists,
botanists, pharmacologists and psychiatrists have
discovered that mind-altering plant substances have
been used in communities ranging from the primitive
to the most modern of societies. The reasons for

these have included the search for greater creativity, as an aid to communication with the supernatural, or simply to provide a culturally acceptable form of escape from the pressures and discomfort of everyday life.

This resourcefulness has manifest itself in a wide variety of skills throughout the ages and it is thousands of years since man first experimented with the naturally occurring substances in his environment in an attempt to relieve pain, overcome anxiety or to alter mood. It is both interesting and relevant to note that two factors are required - the availability of mind-altering substances and the motivation to experiment. In the course of acquiring his experience, man has encountered some substances which have profound effects on his nervous system.

Opium, for example, has been used extensively and continuously since the time of Homer, and as recently as the nineteenth century, it was still widely used in Britain in the form of laudanum to induce sleep or to relieve pain. Among the most vivid accounts of opium abuse ever written was that of Thomas de Quincy in his book 'Confessions of an Opium Eater'. It describes the alternating sensations of pleasure and despair with a degree of conviction which could only stem from hard-won experience.

Cannabis too was known in Central Asia and China as long ago as 3000 B.C. and was first mentioned in the Herbal of the Chinese Emperor Shen Nung.[1]

Mexican cactus buttons, whose active chemical constituent is believed to be mescaline, were used for centuries by the American Indians and coca leaves were chewed by some South American tribes hundreds of years prior to the recognition of the local anaesthetic properties of cocaine (which is contained in the leaves) and its acceptance into medical practice.

Opium, cannabis, mescaline and cocaine are all familiar names of drugs, the abuse of which causes much anxiety to the community and frequently reaches newspaper headlines. However, any substance which alters an individual's behaviour, mental state, mood or physical functions is a drug. Tea, coffee, cocoa and 'cola' drinks all contain the drug caffeine which stimulates mental activity and has an effect on mood as well as performance. The tremendous world-wide popularity of caffeine-containing drinks confirms the view that their

13

effects are generally enjoyed.

Alcohol is another drug with a lengthy and interesting history. Indeed, its history is interlinked with the history of man himself. In ancient times, alcohol was worshipped as a god under a variety of names. Dionysus, for example, was worshipped in Ancient Greece because of his gift of the grape and there were also many Roman temples erected to Bacchus, God of Wine, which are still on view nowadays and attract many tourists throughout the Mediterranean. Today, alcohol continues to be used and abused as a source of chemical comfort in many cultures. It is certainly not regarded as a gift from the Gods at the present time in what has been called the age of pharmacological Calvinism. In the past, the main medical use of alcohol seems to have been as an anaesthetic agent before the introduction of chloroform and ether.

The drinking of ether as a substitute for alcohol has been mentioned in the literature as occurring in situations of deprivation during the nineteenth century in Europe, Great Britain and North America and again during the Second World War in Germany.[2]

One of the most successful temperance crusades of all time was that conducted throughout England, Scotland and Ireland in 1840 by a Roman Catholic priest called Father Matthew[3] but some of his converts, in an attempt to keep to the pledge that they had made, drank ether as a cheap and permissible substitute for alcohol. The intoxicating effect of ether was found to be similar to that achieved by drinking alcohol. There was an added advantage too in that those who used ether could be drunk and sober several times over in less time than it would have taken to become intoxicated on alcohol once and they were still able to honour the actual wording of the pledge if not its spirit.[4] This practice continued to be popular for about 80 years before finally dying out in the 1920s. It has been estimated that in Ireland, Father Matthew's temperance mission caused the consumption of spirits to fall by 23 per cent between 1834 and 1845 but that this had risen again by the 1870s.[5]

This small number of examples is intended to demonstrate that the urge to investigate new experiences, to find a happiness drug or, at the least, to change one's psychological state to a level regarded as desirable is not only one that reaches back into antiquity but is today, a very

widespread, perhaps even universal phenomenon.
Despite the concern in this country regarding young adults who abuse drugs obtained illicitly, it is important to realise that many serious drug problems relate specifically to the use of legally permitted drugs. There is currently much concern about the consumption of alcohol in the United Kingdom and, while it is hard to obtain accurate figures, it is generally believed that men, women and children are drinking increasing amounts. At the same time, there is growing concern about the increasing use and abuse of legally prescribed drugs among the elderly, middle-aged and even younger people. These drugs are mainly, but not exclusively, tranquillisers and hypnotics. What has been established is that overdoses of prescribed drugs such as tranquillisers and hypnotics occur more often in families where abuse of alcohol also constitutes a problem. All of these drugs, including alcohol, depress the function of the brain in various ways.

With the exception of opium and cannabis, which could be smoked, and cocaine, which could be sniffed, the drugs mentioned above were all taken by mouth but recently, some of these drugs have been injected into the body to provide a more immediate effect.

Yet another method of introducing drugs into the body is via the lungs. This is a very effective route and drugs can be given medicinally by the lungs in the form of gases, vapours or aerosols. The general advantage of this route of administration is that the large surface area of the lungs provides easy access to the body and ensures a rapid onset of effect which is almost as quick as that following the intravenous injection of a drug. Such drugs are given preferentially by inhalation during the treatment of certain lung disorders and also as general anaesthetics during surgical operations.

No exhaustive research was required to establish that vapour inhalation, like other forms of drug taking, has a very long and interesting history. The earliest mention of possible vapour inhalation via the lungs is that of the Oracle at Delphi. Throughout the length and breadth of the Ancient Greek world, people venerated the Pythia at Delphi. The Pythia was a priestess of the god Apollo, controlled by priests and temple officials, and was easily accessible to pilgrims who were charged a fee for pronouncement of the oracle. The legend goes that, after many days in preparation, the priestess sat on a tripod over a chasm in the ground and subsequently went into a trance during which her manner became frenzied and she would make utterances which were written down and supplied as the oracular pronouncement in answer to the question posed. There is of course some doubt about the origin of the trances and indeed it has been stated that the Pythia achieved nothing of any importance at any time other than during these episodes. Many authors have noted that the prophesying only occurred when the Pythia was frenzied which raises the question of whether the state was drug induced? One possible source of a drug would appear to be the laurel leaves which the Pythia chewed during the process of foreseeing the future.

Another is more likely and even more interesting. At the particular spot in Delphi where the ruined temple now stands, there was a chasm in the ground. It has been reported that in ancient times goats grazing near this spot began to behave very oddly and bleat in a totally different manner. Eventually, their owner, alarmed about his herd, went to investigate and he also began to behave in a most peculiar fashion and to prophesy future events. Once news of this spread, the same thing also happened with the same dramatic effects on local people who came to investigate the phenomenon. The results, it was said, were not always happy since some people, affected by the trance, threw themselves into the chasm and disappeared for good. Subsequently, one prophetess was chosen to be in sole charge of the oracles (and of the money). One possible explanation of all this unusual behaviour by people and animals alike is that when they were close to the chasm they became intoxicated by inhaling some gas or vapour issuing from the ground.[6]

Although the Oracle at Delphi is the most widely known, Oracles of Apollo were also given at Claros, Didyma and many other places.

All through the social and religious history of most cultures there runs a distinct thread of mysticism, prophesy and worship incorporating in many of them the practical use of vapour inhalation. It appears in the religious cults of Assyria, Babylon, Egypt and Italy to name but a few. Maimonides, the great Hebrew philosopher, is said to have considered incense to be a way of raising the spirits of the priests. Again, during the Renaissance period, Montaigne, the celebrated French writer recommended that physicians should use odours more widely because incenses and perfumes put people in a proper mood for contemplation.[7]

The drinking of liquid ether as a substitute for alcohol has already been mentioned in relation to the temperance movement. However, much earlier, the first known addict to ether by inhalation was thought to be James Graham (1745-1794) who was reported to inhale ether several times a day.[3]

By the nineteenth century, the inhalation of nitrous oxide (often called laughing gas) had become fashionable. The effects were described as good, delightful, intoxicating and relaxing. It was regarded as a genteel way of getting drunk and parties to promote its use increased its popularity. The most famous names linked with it include Coleridge, Roget and Wedgwood. There were also public exhibitions in Britain and America held to demonstrate its effects and, during one of these, it was noted that a man, while under the influence of laughing gas, had sustained several cuts and bruises but had felt no pain. There was also a body of opinion which stated that the use of nitrous oxide was dangerous because animals had almost died during experiments and some people had suffered from giddiness, a slow pulse rate and coma. Fears and uncertainties were therefore expressed about the exact effects of nitrous oxide. In particular, considerable anxiety was voiced about the unconscious state induced in some people who experimented with it.

About the middle of the century, ether appeared as a rival in the field of recreational inhalents and attracted some attention. Sir James Young Simpson (1811-1870) was the first to use ether in midwifery practice in January 1847, although he is more famous for the introduction of chloroform later in that year.

It is interesting to note that, during a visit to Scotland in the summer of 1847, Hans Christian Andersen was a guest of honour in the house of Sir James. Writing in his diary, the Danish author commented that, when everyone had gathered for the evening, some ether was passed round for experimentation. The author did not like the effects of the ether when used for intoxication at the party and commented adversely on the lifeless eyes of the ladies but he recognised at the same time the incredible potential for the relief of pain during operations.[8] Once again, as in the case of nitrous oxide, there was much opposition to the use of ether in clinical practice.

Before long, chloroform had entered the stakes as an agent for intoxication. It is interesting to note that nitrous oxide, ether and chloroform were all inhaled via the lungs in order that people would become intoxicated, and that these substances could be used in this way because they are either gases or volatile liquids which give off a concentrated vapour. It is also quite clear that if these drugs had not been capable of producing intoxication they would not have been so extensively investigated at that time. Indeed, modern anaesthesia and the development of high-technology surgery have come about directly because \of man's perpetual quest for new experiences from mind-altering drugs.

Although experimentation goes back a long time, the abuse of volatile substances by adults has not disappeared altogether during this century. It would seem to have been absent for a few decades and then to have occurred infrequently and sporadically when it did reappear. Isolated reports concerning individual cases of chloroform inhalation[9] gasoline or petrol sniffing[10,11] and nitrous oxide sniffing[12] have all appeared in the medical literature.

The types of individuals most often involved in this abuse are likely to be those with easy access to suitable volatile substances at work, in laboratories, in factories or in the operating theatres of hospitals. People serving prison sentences and those suffering from emotional or psychological disorders would also seem to be more involved in the practice.[13,14]

However, in a study conducted during a four month period in 1980 of 160 adult patients with drug related problems, six (4 per cent) were found to be related to solvent abuse. The choice of substances in such cases always depended on their immediate availability. The age range was found to be 17 to 33 years with an average of 26 years. The American researchers suggest that solvent abuse in adults is more common than is generally thought and they also suggest that solvents should be considered in relation to acutely intoxicated adults, especially where the tests for drugs prove to be negative.[15]

This book deals with the deliberate misuse of volatile chemicals, not by industrial workers, laboratory technicians, anaesthetists or by persons

incarcerated by the state but by young people.
The first cases to be described involved the
inhalation of gasoline fumes by young people in
America. The term 'gasoline sniffing' has been used
to describe this practice since it involves the
inhalation of the vapours from petrol (gasoline in
America). It was not confined to America since
there were reports published in the 1950s, 1960s
and 1970s of sporadic petrol sniffing in Australia,
India and Great Britain. In view of the wide
availability of petrol to young people and the fact
that its vapours could often be inhaled at no cost,
it might have been expected to have widespread, if
not universal appeal. However, only 20-30 cases
have been recorded. The available information
relates entirely to a small number of case reports
on children who were referred for psychiatric
evaluation and management. This referral to
psychiatric agencies was due to odd behaviour,
hallucinations or unusual and unexpected temper
tantrums.[16,17,18,19] In some cases, the clinical
presentation was similar to that seen in people who
had taken drugs such as LSD. One case strongly
resembled schizophrenia and was originally misdiag-
nosed as such before gasoline sniffing was
discovered to be the cause of the symptoms. These
reports gave the information that the individuals
had been involved for periods ranging from five
months to seven years and yet had remained
undetected in the community. It should also be
noted that the gasoline sniffing was entirely
unexpected in these cases, that the agencies to
whom they were presented were medical and that it
was the unusual pattern of behaviour which led to
the referrals initially.
In most of the reported cases, it seems to
have been the case that the discovery of the
intoxicating effects of gasoline sniffing was
initially accidental. This sometimes occurred when
they were working with cars[17] or lawnmowers. Some
were introduced to the practice by their friends
but long after their friends stopped gasoline
sniffing they continued in the practice.[18,19] There
was one recorded case of a child, addicted to
eating rubber erasers, who switched deliberately to
gasoline sniffing as an alternative[20] and another
who had been sniffing trichloroethylene and later
found gasoline sniffing a suitable alternative when
the trichloroethylene became unavailable.[21]
In the world literature, only three cases of
female involvement in gasoline sniffing have been

reported[21,22,23] and it would seem therefore to have been an almost exclusively male activity. Gasoline sniffing is said to have been particularly prevalent in rural areas[24,25] because of its ready availability together with the lack of suitable diversions. Despite this, most of the cases reported were from urban areas.

Two prevalence studies of gasoline sniffing were carried out, one on Elcho Island, a remote island in northern Australia, in 1968[26] and one in a village school in New Mexico.[27] The results of the two studies indicated that gasoline sniffing had been a group activity and that the extent of the involvement was small.

It seems clear, from the world literature, that gasoline sniffing occurred sporadically, in the main infrequently, and that it did not at any time constitute a large problem numerically. The individuals who came to attention did so because of behaviour problems which were initially investigated for a psychiatric origin.

Midway through the twentieth century, and overlapping gasoline sniffing, reports of glue sniffing appeared in print. In Tuscon, Arizona and Pueblo, Colorado, the press reported the arrests of children who were suspected of sniffing glue. Subsequently, two reporters wrote an article on glue sniffing which was published in the magazine supplement of the Denver Sunday Post in August 1959. There was subsequently a tremendous wave of publicity about glue sniffing with repeated warnings against it appearing in newspapers and on television. Ten months later, it was said, Denver had an enormous glue sniffing problem largely involving children and young adolescents.[28]

Again, to be specific, glue sniffing involves the inhalation of the vapours from some solvent-based glues and many reports of this new fad were made throughout the 1960s. The literature on this latest form of inhalant misuse is mainly based on information about groups of 'sniffers' who came to the attention of various community agencies such as the police, youth counsellors, doctors and psychiatrists. The events which brought these young people to the attention of such professional groups were varied. For example there were anti-social activities linked with the sniffing episodes, there were psychiatric appointments[29] or morbidity severe enough to justify hospital admissions and there were sudden deaths.

As in the cases of gasoline sniffing, it is

possible that the first experience of the effects of the inhalation of the fumes from glue was accidental. For example, children building model kits may have discovered in the process that they could become drunk and some may have continued to indulge deliberately because they liked the effect.[30] In other cases, children might well have been introduced to glue sniffing by their friends at school or in their neighbourhood.

Although Denver, Colorado appears to have been the first city in the world to suffer what could be termed a serious glue sniffing problem, other American cities were subsequently affected and by 1965 glue sniffing was said to be occurring in every state in the United States of America.[31] It is not clear whether the practice spread from one place to another or whether it started spontaneously in many places at about the same time.

While gasoline sniffing seems to have been the first kind of inhalant misuse on the contemporary scene and glue sniffing the most widely reported in the press, there were also reports of a variety of other products being exploited on account of their intoxicating vapour content. These have included nail polish remover,[32] anti-freeze,[33] chloroform,[9] marking pencils, lacquer thinners, paint thinners[31] and aerosol products. To the potential sniffer, a whole range of products containing easily inhaled, intoxicating chemicals was readily available in America and elsewhere. If one product became unavailable for any reason, another could always be found as an alternative without difficulty.

These products were misused, not because of their smell, but because their vapours induced intoxication and other apparently similar products which did not cause intoxication were ignored. A good example of this is that of adhesives. Commercially available adhesives are of three main classes: (1) Non-volatile adhesives; (2) Aqueous adhesives; (3) Solvent-based adhesives. Only solvent-based adhesives have been deliberately inhaled because they alone can intoxicate when abused and the other categories can be discounted.[34]

Those solvents commonly found in adhesives which are capable of producing intoxication when present in sufficient concentrations are toluene, hexanes, heptanes, ethyl acetate, isopropyl acetate, acetone, methyl ethyl ketone, methylene chloride and trichloroethane.[34] Cleaning fluids usually contain one or more of the following - trichloroethylene, perchloroethylene, trichloroethane

and carbon tetrachloride.[11,35] Lighter fuels were
found to contain a mixture of aliphatic hydrocarbons
and nail polish remover to contain acetone and
aliphatic acetates.[32,36] Petrol is not a solvent
but a volatile mixture of hydrocarbons. Ether and
chloroform are volatile liquids used as anaesthetic
agents. Most commercial aerosols use liquified gas
as the propellant but dissolved gases may also be
used. The components of an aerosol are its active
constituents, a solvent system and liquified gases.[37]
    Solvent abuse involves the deliberate inhalation
of substances which can be absorbed into the body
via the lungs and which produce an intoxicated
state. This method of becoming drunk could more
generally be described as 'inhalant misuse' since
any such substance has to be in a form which is
suitable for inhaling into the lungs. The substance
therefore can be a gas, such as nitrous oxide or
butane, or it can be the vapour of a volatile
liquid such as ether, petrol or toluene. The
extensive misuse of volatile liquids has given rise
to the term 'volatile substance abuse' to describe
the practice.[38] Many of the volatile liquids, such
as toluene, trichloroethylene or acetone, are used
as solvents in paints, cleaning materials or glues
and this has led to the adoption of the name
'solvent abuse'. Because the misuse of solvents in
glues has been very common, the term 'glue
sniffing' has been widely applied. In all of these
cases the employment of the words misuse or abuse
is amply justified since the substance or the
product which contains it is not used for the
specific purpose for which it was intended. It is
much less important to get the name correct than it
is to understand what the term implies.
    Products such as aerosols, solvent-based
adhesives and dry-cleaning substances are all
perfectly safe when used normally and it is only
when the vapours are deliberately inhaled in
sufficient concentration to cause intoxication that
problems arise.
    Children and adolescents have been involved in
the misuse of various volatile substances not just
in America but in places as far scattered as
Africa, Australia, Canada, Finland, Japan, Mexico,
South America and Western Europe.[2,35,39,40,41]
    In 1964, a Winnipeg pharmacist noticed that
the sale of a popular brand of nail varnish had
rocketed. The teenagers who flocked to buy it
admitted that they intended to inhale its vapours
'for kicks'. Although accurate figures were

impossible to obtain, it was estimated by 1966 that between 2 and 6 per cent of all school children in Winnipeg were involved in the practice of sniffing the vapours from nail varnish.[32]

This was still at a comfortable distance from Britain but in the course of an article in the British Medical Journal in 1967, a psychiatrist stated that although glue sniffing was not known to be a problem in Great Britain, the easy access to, and availability of, the agents used made it not unlikely that the problem might arise at some point in the future.[42] A few years after this, the Annual Report of the Bradford Drug Addiction Liaison Committee commented on the case histories of six youths, five of whom had been referred through the school health service, because of their involvement in glue sniffing. All had been investigated and were said to show evidence of liver damage. In November 1970, the abuse of industrial chemicals by young people, with resulting intoxicated behaviour, was detected by the police in Lanarkshire. Since then, inhalant misuse has become much more widespread, both in terms of numbers and also in the wide variety of products which have been abused for their vapour components. It is now quite clear that the practice has occurred, however sporadically or infrequently, throughout the length and breadth of Britain.

The conclusions are clear. Many substances have been inhaled by man throughout the centuries to alter his mental state. No age can boast immunity from their use or abuse, from the Pythia at Delphi, down through the years to the 'ether frolics' and 'chloroform jags' of a more modern student population and finally to the abuse of industrial solvents and other materials by young people in urban industrial Scotland and elsewhere. It is clear that man's desire to experiment with substances of all kinds to change his state of consciousness is universal and that inhalation of vapours or gases is an ancient manifestation of this phenomenon.

## REFERENCES

1. Taylor, Russell W.J. (1971), 'History and pharmacology of psychedelic drugs', Internationale Zeitschrift fur Klinische Pharmacologie, Therapie und Toxikologie, 5(1), 51-7.

2. Blatherwick, C.E. (1968), 'Understanding glue sniffing', Canadian Journal of Public Health, 63, 272-5.

3. Nagle, D.R. (1968), 'Anaesthetic addiction and drunkenness: a contemporary and historical survey', International Journal of the Addictions, 3(1), 25-39.

4. Kerr, N. (1968), 'Ether drinking', Drug Dependence, 15-19.

5. Spring, J.A. and Buss, D.H. (1977), 'Three centuries of alcohol in the British diet', Nature, 270(5638), 567-72.

6. Flaceliere, R. (1976), Greek Oracles, Elek Books, London.

7. Preble, E. and Laury, G.V. (1967), 'The ten cent hallucinogen', International Journal of the Addictions, 2(2), 700-2.

8. Secher, O. (1971), 'Simpson and Hans Andersen', British Medical Journal, 4, 814.

9. Weinraub, M., Groce, P. and Karno, M. (1972), 'Chloroformism - a new case of a bad old habit', California Medicine, 117, 63-5.

10. Karani, V. (1966), 'Peripheral neuritis after addiction to petrol', British Medical Journal, 1, 216.

11. Malcolm, A.I. (1968), 'Solvent sniffing and its effects', Addictions, 15, 12-21.

12. Danto, B.L. (1964), 'A bag full of laughs', American Journal of Psychiatry, 212, 612-13.

13. Ahmed, M.M. (1971), 'Ocular effects of antifreeze poisoning', British Journal of Ophthalmology, 55, 854-5.

14. Man, P.L. (1969), 'Case report of a paint thinner sniffer', Journal of the Kentucky Medical Association, 67, 195-7 and 230.

15. Hershey, C.O. and Miller, S. (1982), 'Solvent abuse: a shift to adults', International Journal of the Addictions, 17(6), 1085-9.

16. Bethell, M.F. (1965), 'Toxic psychosis caused by inhalation of petrol fumes', British Medical Journal, 2(1), 276-7.

17. Black, P.D. (1967), 'Mental illness due to the voluntary inhalation of petrol vapour', Medical Journal of Australia, 2, 70-1.

18. Gold, N. (1963), 'Self intoxication by petrol vapour inhalation', Medical Journal of Australia, 50, 582-4.
19. Tolan, E.J. and Lingl , F.A. (1964), '"Model Psychosis" produced by inhalation of gasoline fumes', American Journal of Psychiatry, 120, 757-61.
20. Grant, W.B. (1962), 'Inhalation of gasoline fumes by a child', Psychiatric Quarterly, 36, 555-7.
21. Oldham, W. (1961), 'Deliberate self-intoxication with petrol vapour', British Medical Journal, 2, 1687-8.
22. Lawton, J.J. and Malmquist, C.P. (1961), 'Gasoline addiction in children', Psychiatric Quarterly, 35, 555.
23. Schmitt, R.C., Goolishian, H.A. and Abston, S. (1972), 'Gasoline sniffing in children leading to severe burn injury', Journal of Paediatrics, 80, 1021-3.
24. Voegele, G.E. and Dietze, H.J. (1963), 'Addiction to gasoline smelling in juvenile delinquents', British Journal of Criminology, 4, 43-60.
25. Edwards, R.V. (1960), 'Case report of gasoline sniffing', American Journal of Psychiatry, 117, 555-7.
26. Nurcombe, B., Bianchi, G.N., Money, J. and Cawte, J.E. (1970), 'A hunger for stimuli: the psychosocial background of petrol inhalation', British Journal of Medical Psychology, 43, 367-74.
27. Kaufman, A. (1973), 'Gasoline sniffing among children in a Pueblo Indian village', Paediatrics, 51(6), 1060-4.
28. Brecher, E.M. (1972), Licit and Illicit Drugs, Part VI, 'Inhalants, solvents and glue sniffing', Little, Brown and Co., Boston.
29. Press, E. (1963), 'Glue sniffing', Journal of Paediatrics, 63(3), 516-18.
30. Glaser, H.H. and Massengale, O.N. (1962), 'Glue sniffing in children', Journal of the American Medical Association, 181, 300-3.
31. Corliss, L.M. (1965), 'A review of evidence on glue sniffing - a persistent problem', Journal of School Health, 35, 442-9.
32. Gellman, V. (1968), 'Glue sniffing among Winnipeg school children', Canadian Medical Association Journal, 98, 411-13.
33. Guaraldi, G.P. and Bonasegla, F. (1968), 'Su di un caso di tossicomania da tricloroetilene', Rivista Sperimentale di Freniatria, 92, 913-20.

34. Ackerman, H.E. (1982), 'The constitution of adhesives and its relationship to solvent abuse', Human Toxicology, 1(3), 223-30.
35. Cohen, S. (1973), 'The volatile solvents', Public Health Reviews, II(2), 185-214.
36. Ackerly, W.C. and Gibson, G. (1966), 'Lighter fluid "sniffing"', American Journal of Psychiatry, 120, 1056-61.
37. Roberts, D.J. (1982), 'Abuse of aerosol products by inhalation', Human Toxicology, 1(3), 231-8.
38. Anderson, H.R., Dick, B., Macnair, R.S., Palmer, J.C. and Ramsey, J.D. (1982), 'An investigation of 140 deaths associated with volatile substance abuse in the United Kingdom 1971-1981', Human Toxicology, 1(3), 207-21.
39. Alha, A., Korte, T and Tenhu, M. (1973), 'Solvent sniffing death', Rechtsmedizen, 72(4), 299-305.
40. Goto, I., Matsumura, M., Inoui, N., Murai, V., Shida, K., Santa, J., and Kuroiwa, Y. (1976), 'Toxic polyneuropathy due to glue sniffing', Journal of Neurology, Neurosurgery and Psychiatry, 37(7), 843-53.
41. Shirabe, T., Tsudo, T., Terao, A. and Arake, S. (1974), 'Toxic polyneuropathy due to glue sniffing', Journal of Neurological Sciences, 21(1), 101-13.
42. Merry, J. and Zachariadis, N. (1962), 'Addiction to glue sniffing', British Medical Journal, 2, 1448.

Chapter Three

THE PRACTICE OF SOLVENT ABUSE

Background Review

Available information on solvent abuse prior to the
1970s was based mainly on case reports of small
isolated groups of individuals. They had drawn
attention to themselves on account of some
associated factor such as disturbed behaviour
patterns, accidents while intoxicated or anti-social
acts of disorderly conduct directly linked with
sniffing episodes. Much of the available literature
on solvent abuse comes from America and most of the
original American referrals came from police or
social agencies in urban areas. To the potential
sniffer in America, there was readily available a
wide variety of substances with volatile components.
The substances specifically singled out for abuse
were chosen because of their capacity to intoxicate,
their availability and the fact that they were
cheap. Several authors have stated that sniffers
sometimes showed a marked preference for a
particular type of substance, although, if for any
reason, it could not be procured, another could
usually be found as a suitable alternative[1,2,3]
     The methods employed in solvent abuse not only
varied according to the type of product but in many
cases were quite sophisticated. Petrol sniffing had
occurred on the spot and directly from the tank or
container without any additional equipment.
However, when vapours from adhesives were abused, a
waxed paper bag or a plastic bag sometimes served
as a dispenser.[4,5] Liquid substances were often
poured on to a rag which, when saturated, was
pressed against the nose.[6] Aerosol products
required no special equipment for their abuse.[7,8]
     Although solvent abuse was sometimes a
solitary act, it appeared to occur much more

27

frequently as a group activity[9,10] which led in some cases to the organisation of sniffing parties.[11,12,13] The group nature of the activity may have led to its initial detection but it also provided something of a safety factor. There were obvious practical advantages in the arrangement since some members of the group could alert the others to the possibility of detection. Again, in the event of an overdose or sudden physical emergency involving any one of the group, help could be more easily summoned and a tragedy thereby averted.

Records indicate that the degree to which these individuals were involved varied considerably. Some experimented merely because it was the current 'craze'[5,14] but others indulged in regular and more prolonged sniffing episodes which extended over periods varying in length from one month to several years.[9,15,16,17]

Despite the fact that the problem was said to have been of epidemic proportions in some places at some times, it is extremely hard to find statistics which support that claim. Indeed, it was reassuring to find that, even in America, solvent abuse represented in the main what amounted to a short experimental phase in the lives of a small proportion of children and young people.


Terms Used
'Solvent abuse', 'inhalant misuse' and 'glue sniffing' are all terms used to describe the deliberate inhalation via the lungs of substances to induce intoxication. Although the term 'inhalant misuse' is the most general of these terms, the term 'solvent abuse' is used throughout this book to describe the practice because the very first incidents to come to light in Strathclyde were those which involved industrial solvents. The exactness of the term applied to the activity is much less important than an understanding of the activity itself and so the term 'solvent abuse', first coined by the police dealing with the early incidents, has been retained.


Use and Abuse
Initial police descriptions of solvent abuse within Lanarkshire did not make clear which substances were involved or by what methods they were being misused. Later reports named industrial solvents

28

followed by a variety of household materials but, even then, there was some confusion as to what was happening or why so much professional energy was being directed towards what appeared to be an occasional sniffing of products with a whole range of legitimate uses. Normal users expect and indeed demand to have at their disposal a wide range of household products with which to stick materials together, remove stains, condition fabrics, polish furniture and so on. There are many millions of buyers of such products world-wide and the number of uses to which they put them are endless. Could such people be at risk from the ordinary usage of such products? The answer was an emphatic 'no'. These products have a wide range of applications and safely fulfil many useful functions when properly applied. The difference between normal use and teenage abuse was well highlighted in a letter sent by Lanarkshire's Medical Officer of Health to all general practitioners in Lanarkshire in 1973. The letter was dated 28th February 1973.

Dear Doctor,

I should like to alert you to a situation which has serious consequences to the health of young people at secondary schools. There are certain commercial products which are used for dry cleaning and for the removal of stains and grease. There are also products which are adhesive agents. These are freely available in shops and they are a great boon for 'do it yourself' jobs in the home.

It is to their incorrect use I wish to draw your attention. Most of these products contain a mixture of solvents such as acetone, chloroform, carbon tetrachloride, trichloroethylene and perchloroethylene. These solvents are volatile and when the vapour is deliberately and constantly inhaled it can cause toxic effects, mainly on the brain, liver and kidneys. I know of two cases recently, one a schoolboy, where the outcome was fatal.

I wish to emphasise that commercial products containing these solvents are entirely safe when used strictly according to the instructions on the container and strictly for the purpose for which they were intended. It has, however, come to my notice that there is an increasing trend among young people at senior schools to use these products in a way that may be harmful to their health.

Medical Officer of Health

## Sources of Information

Most of the information presented in this book has been gathered from studies carried out in the Glasgow and Lanark Divisions of Strathclyde and a short geographical description of the area may be useful to the reader. Strathclyde is the largest of the Scottish regions and was formed in the mid-1970s from the City of Glasgow and all or most of the old local government areas of Lanarkshire, Ayrshire, Renfrewshire, Dunbarton and Argyll. Glasgow has a population of just under one million. Like many industrial cities that developed during the nineteenth century, it now has severe problems of industrial and urban decay. Lanarkshire, now the Lanark Division of Strathclyde, is adjacent to Glasgow and has a population of over half a million. It contains a number of industrial towns, villages from a now vanished coal industry and agricultural areas. Many of the towns form part of the industrial hinterland of Glasgow and therefore share many of its social problems.

From 1970 onwards, information about solvent abuse has come from various groups of professional people, some in Lanarkshire where the practice was first seen and others in Glasgow or elsewhere in Strathclyde. In some instances, problems of intoxicated behaviour have drawn attention to the solvent abuse which precipitated it and, in other cases, the theft of substances has involved the police. The practice has, at different times and at varying levels, attracted the concern of a range of professional people to deal with behaviour problems associated with solvent abuse. Those who have been involved in this way have been social workers, List D school staff, youth counsellors, psychologists and psychiatrists. Doctors and nurses working in community clinics, in general practice and in hospitals have also been involved in the medical aspects of the problem such as coma, accidents and medical emergencies caused by acute toxic effects.

Much of the available information from these sources was anecdotal or referred specifically to individual cases but systematic studies of the problem within the community in Strathclyde have been conducted since 1973. These have involved contact with young people who had indulged or were still involved in the practice and also with their parents. In particular, much detailed factual information has been obtained about the actual practice of solvent abuse from the young people involved.

A study was undertaken of 102 children who had come to the attention of the Lanarkshire police between 1971 and 1973 on account of their solvent abuse. A control group of 102 non-sniffing children was found and matched with the sniffers for age, sex and home area. This allowed some comparisons to be made between the two groups.

A more detailed investigation of the practice of solvent abuse was later carried out in Lanarkshire between January and July 1975 using 84 individuals who had been referred by social workers, police and parents for assessment. A control group of 84 children who were not involved in solvent abuse were matched for age, sex and home area. Again, this made it possible to compare the two groups.

A further study to determine features of solvent abuse such as the time of day or the day of the week when it most often occurred was carried out over a six month period in Lanarkshire in 1976. 42 children were seen, most within one to one and a half hours of their glue sniffing sessions.

A survey to determine the extent of solvent abuse among boys in a comprehensive school in the East End of Glasgow was conducted in 1976 and subsequently repeated in 1979 and 1982.

In 1978, in a police station in the East End of Glasgow, a clinic was set up to collect detailed information on solvent abuse and to assess, if possible, the extent of the problem among children in that area. It had facilities for screening individuals involved in solvent abuse for signs of physical damage and thereby provided information for the various professional groups in the East End who were concerned about the practice.

A study of 400 cases seen in Glasgow between 1975 and 1981 added further detailed knowledge about the actual practice of solvent abuse and also about its implications.

55 regular abusers of solvents were the subjects of a detailed study carried out between 1981 and 1984 and, as a result, a large amount of factual information was collected from individuals who were clearly very experienced in these matters.

The accumulated information from all these

31

sources has made it possible to describe accurately the practice of solvent abuse including the range of substances associated with it, the methods employed and the extent and severity of involvement. Information has also been obtained from the British Adhesives and Sealants Association and from the Department of Forensic Medicine of the University of Glasgow. In this way, and from these sources, the available data from Strathclyde have been collected and collated in order to present the reader with as much information about the practice as is considered ethical to put into print.

## Results in Strathclyde

### Products

Many substances have been deliberately selected for misuse because of their capacity to cause intoxication when inhaled in a sufficiently high concentration. The first two dozen cases in Lanarkshire involved industrial trichloroethylene which had been stolen by young people from steel-works where it was used as a degreasing agent. When access to this source was successfully stopped by the police, the next substances to be abused were industrial perchloroethylene, rubber cement and paint thinners. The perchloroethylene had been stolen from dry-cleaning establishments and the rubber cement and paint thinners from garages in various parts of Lanarkshire. Access to these substances was stopped by the Chief Constable of Lanarkshire who wrote to the owners of garages and dry cleaners informing them of the situation but there was an immediate shift to domestic dry-cleaning fluids and shoe conditioner. This time, the substances were purchased or stolen from shops.

Finally, when access to these substances was curtailed by shopkeepers who operated a voluntary ban on the products involved, commercial adhesives began to be abused and, by 1975, they had replaced the other substances in popularity. This was partly because they were so readily accessible when other substances were no longer available but also because solvent abuse had become much more widespread in Lanarkshire between 1970 and 1975 (Table 3.1).

An attempt was made to restrict the access of young people to solvent-based adhesives. Non-volatile glues and water-based glues were not included since

Table 3.1: The Shift Between Substances in Lanarkshire 1970 - 1975

| Substance | The number of detected cases of abuse of different products | | | | | |
|---|---|---|---|---|---|---|
| | 1970 | 1971 | 1972 | 1973 | 1974 | 1975 |
| Tricholoro ethylene | 11 | 14 | – Access stopped | – | – | – |
| Perchloro ethylene | – | 28 | 1 | – Access stopped | – | – |
| Rubber cement | – | 2 | 6 | Voluntary ban | – | – |
| Shoe conditioner | – | 8 | 17 | 1 Voluntary ban | – | – |
| Petrol | 1 | 1 | – | 1 | – | – |
| Ether | – | – | 2 | – | – | – |
| Chloroform | – | – | – | 6 | – | – |
| Acetone | – | – | – | 3 | – | – |
| Paint thinners | – | – | 7 | 1 | – | – |
| Dry-cleaning fluid | – | – | 11 | 10 | 12 | 29 |
| Adhesives | – | – | – | 91 | 68 | 202 |

- indicates no cases were found

they were not abused due to the lack of intoxicating effect when inhaled. However, legitimate users still required access to solvent-based glues because of their many uses in the home and elsewhere. In some shops, solvent-based adhesives were removed from the open shelves and in other cases they were sold only if they were bought along with other purchases which indicated that the glue was intended for some proper purpose. For example, rubber cement might be sold with a pair of stick-on soles for shoes. Another policy was to insist that young people should bring along a note from parents which indicated that the glue was required for some domestic purpose. Unfortunately, forged notes, supposedly from parents or teachers, were sometimes a problem. This voluntary ban seems to have had some effect in reducing access although young people who were anxious to maintain their supply simply travelled further afield than their local area in order to obtain glues. Again, there remained the problem that not all shopkeepers approved of or operated the voluntary ban. However, by 1974, reduced access to adhesives in the shops in certain areas of Lanarkshire due to the voluntary ban was noticeable even to adult members of the community. Many of them, including the author, can vouch for this fact because of the difficulties encountered when attempting to purchase adhesives for legitimate purposes.

Petrol sniffing occurred only sporadically between 1970 and 1975. Acetone, ether and chloroform were also abused. The acetone and ether were stolen from school laboratories on two separate occasions and the inhalation of these resulted in detection. The chloroform was stolen on one occasion during a conducted tour of a hospital by a school party and the vapour from it was inhaled by six girls.

Apart from the abuse of these products, which took place in isolated and specific cases, solvent abuse followed a pattern. The effect of making one substance unavailable for one reason or another led invariably to the abuse of other products for their intoxicating properties. The various moves from one substance to another in Lanarkshire between 1970 and 1975 can be seen in Table 3.1.

So far, the information quoted in this book about the substances abused has come from agencies who were aware of the problem. However, since 1975 information about the substances abused has been obtained directly from the children themselves along with other details of the practice.

During a study of 84 Lanarkshire children seen by the author in 1975, it was found that 87 per cent of them had used adhesives, 11 per cent had employed dry-cleaning fluids obtained from shops or home and 2 per cent had used both kinds of products from time to time.[18] A large study of 400 cases conducted by the author between 1975 and 1981 in Glasgow showed that in 89 per cent of cases, various proprietary brands of adhesives were misused. Other substances involved were dry-cleaning fluids, hair lacquer and the contents of fire extinquishers.[19]

A study of 300 children who attended the clinic in the East End of Glasgow between 1978 and December 1980 showed that all attending had used proprietary brands of adhesives while only one had used a dry-cleaning compound and there were no cases of aerosol abuse.[20]

In a study of 55 individuals who had been involved in solvent abuse on a regular basis for periods varying from 10 months to 7 years, it was found by the author that 53 of them had abused solvent-based adhesives and that two had abused butane gas.

Of course, it is only possible to quote the findings from actual cases seen by investigators or by members of professional agencies and it is unwise to make general statements about solvent abuse since there may be a number of other people indulging in the practice whose involvement never comes to attention and who consequently remain undetected. What has been described here is what has so far come to light. As a result, it is possible to state authoritatively that it is solvents in adhesives which have been most frequently abused over the past ten years in the West of Scotland. There have been verbal reports of a recent trend towards butane and aerosol abuse but these have not been confirmed to date.

## Methods of Abuse

Each of the substances involved was abused because of its ability to intoxicate. Other apparently similar products which lacked the ability to intoxicate were ignored. Legitimate users of any product of course are not affected by its constituents when it is used properly. In order to increase the concentration and thereby increase the intoxicating effects, a variety of methods have been employed in the West of Scotland by those involved in solvent abuse.

Methods of inhalation have varied from time to time and from place to place and have ranged from the very crude to the very sophisticated.

Information, and presumably misinformation, about the matter are duly passed along the juvenile grapevine.

Most young people when inhaling the fumes from trichloroethylene or from perchloroethylene, simply poured these liquids into empty soft-drinks bottles and inhaled the fumes from the open end. This meant that only a low concentration would be obtained and that there would be a constant dilution by the fresh air. Petrol vapours were also inhaled directly from the container as were those from ether, acetone and chloroform and it is logical to assume that the same low concentration would be achieved.

When the vogue for inhaling shoe conditioner fumes and household dry-cleaning products replaced these substances in popularity, a more sophisticated method was developed to enhance the effects. A rag or handkerchief was saturated with the volatile liquid and held over the nose and mouth. Sometimes the simpler method of inhaling fumes from the top of the bottle was still used for domestic dry-cleaning fluids and nail polish remover.

Originally, adhesives had been inhaled by being poured or squeezed on to a rag or handkerchief which was then held as a pad over the nose and mouth but by 1974, in Lanarkshire and thereafter in the rest of the West of Scotland, small plastic or polythene bags were used. A chosen amount of the intoxicating substance was poured or squeezed into the bag and the open end of the bag was held over the nose and mouth to provide a good fit, thus concentrating the vapours and reducing the dilution by fresh air.[19] This is now by far the most popular method of inhaling toluene fumes from adhesives in many communities in Britain today. With care the bags can be made to last for three to four hours, although their walls are pulled together as the adhesive dries. In a few cases in Glasgow, the adhesive was placed in a container such as a milk bottle or jar and the vapours were inhaled from the open end.

Other techniques have been developed over the years to increase the effects but the details of these have been deliberately excluded from this book by the author to avoid giving such information to any young persons tempted to experiment. This exclusion is both deliberate and necessary since many of these more sophisticated methods have proved to be dangerous. It must be pointed out that this has applied in only a small number of cases

which created acute emergencies. Readers requiring more details are directed to work published
elsewhere.[18,19]

## The Chemicals

It is important to understand that it is not the
substance itself which is inhaled but the vapour
from its volatile components. There are many such
chemicals which can intoxicate by gaining access to
the body via the lungs and these are discussed in
Chapter 6. While they vary in their effectiveness
in producing intoxication, they all act quickly and
this is perhaps one of their attractions.

## Knowledge of Solvent Abuse

The young people, having demonstrated their ability
to seek out substances capable of producing
intoxication, then proceeded to develop methods to
enhance the effects. The information obtained from
a number of incidents indicated clearly that they
had become quite expert and this created a problem
for some professional people. For example, some
children, when interviewed, expressed a preference
for the solvent-based glue out of one shop as
compared to the same brand from another shop. It
transpired that because the first shop had a much
quicker turnover of stock than the other the
intoxicating effect of the adhesive bought from it
would be greater because less solvent would have
evaporated into the atmosphere prior to the
children buying it. The young people's knowledge of
solvent abuse is discussed further in Chapter 4.

## The Practice

It was obvious from information given by the police
that most of the individuals who had come to their
attention in connection with solvent abuse had done
so partly because of the group nature of their
activity. In the study of 102 children who had come
to the attention of the police in Lanarkshire
between 1971 and 1973, it was found that solvent
abuse occurred as a solitary activity in a small
proportion of the cases (5 per cent) and that in
the remainder it was found to involve groups.[21]
Most of the groups involved males only (56 per cent
of the cases) although there were mixed groups of
males and females (27 per cent) and also some
groups that were female only.

The study of the 84 individual cases seen in 1975 indicated that only 5 per cent had indulged entirely on their own at that time. A large majority (83 per cent) practiced solvent abuse as a group activity while a few (12 per cent) indulged in groups at some times and preferred to do it on their own at other times.

In a large study of 400 cases seen between 1975 and 1981 in Glasgow, it was again found that 5 per cent had practised solitary sniffing only whereas the vast majority (85 per cent) were always involved in it exclusively as a group practice.[19]

In a recently completed study of 55 habitual sniffers who had been involved regularly for long periods ranging from ten months to seven years, it was found that 7 per cent had practised the habit on a solitary basis, 31 per cent had always been involved with a group, and 31 per cent of them sometimes indulged on their own and sometimes with a group. The remaining 31 per cent had first been involved with their peer group but had continued the practice on their own long after the other members of the group had stopped.

The group nature of solvent abuse was much less in evidence in this study of regular sniffers and this would indicate the presence of factors other than peer group pressure. The groups of chronic abusers were strikingly different in both structure and purpose from the groups of young people who indulged in the practice for a short time as a social and peer group activity. Again, this is discussed further in Chapter 4.


Seasonal Variation
It had been suggested that there might be some seasonal variation which could affect the level of solvent abuse. A careful study of the police statistics on solvent abuse in Lanarkshire collected between 1971 and 1973 indicated that this might be the case. February showed the highest level of cases (30 per cent) followed by November (17 per cent). Using a similar number of non-sniffing controls who had come to the attention of the police in the same period, it was found that the referrals were evenly spread throughout the year. However, more detailed clinical studies from 1975 onwards indicated that this apparent seasonal variation of solvent abuse was due to variation of the detection rate.

Day of Referral
A study was undertaken in 1976 of 42 cases referred
by the police immediately following a sniffing
session.[22] The purpose was to establish details
about the practice with particular reference to the
day or days of the week preferred and to the times
of day. It was found that most cases were detected
on Mondays (26 per cent), Wednesdays (24 per cent)
and Thursdays (26 per cent). No cases were detected
on Sundays and only 2 per cent on Saturdays. Figure
3.1 demonstrates these findings.

Figure 3.1: Days of the Week on which Cases Were Referred

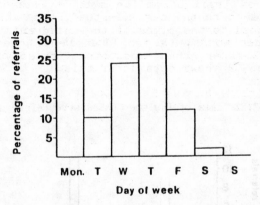

Source: by kind permission of The Editor, The Lancet.

The apparent absence of solvent abuse at weekends
has two reasonable interpretations. Firstly, it is
possible that individuals did not abuse solvents so
frequently at weekends because increased parental
supervision made it more difficult or alternative
activities, such as football, youth clubs, the
cinema, discos and so on, might be more readily
available and more attractive. Secondly, it is
possible that the figures reflected a variation in
the detection rate rather than in the incidence
rate, the police being busier at weekends with
drunk drivers, assaults and road accidents. The
author's inability to interpret these statistics
with any certainty reflects the enormous difficulties
encountered in trying to quantify information about
the incidence of solvent abuse.

Time of Referral
It was clear from this study that approximately half of the cases were referred during the evenings, the remainder being referred during the mornings or afternoons. This indicated that solvent abuse represented some kind of evening social activity in half of the cases but, in the remainder, it seemed to be an alternative to attending school although it was not possible to tell from this study whether the solvent abuse had occurred before or after the truancy.

There were periods during the day when no referrals were made. Since these coincided with meal times, it might be thought that they were due to a low level of police activity but this turned out not to be the case. Instead, they were found to be linked to the times of the children's own meals. In other words, the children went home for their meals rather than indulging in solvent abuse. Figure 3.2 shows details of this.

Figure 3.2: Times of Day when Cases were Referred

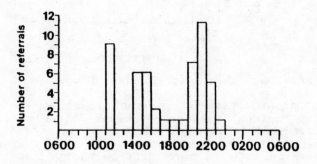

Source: by kind permission of The Editor, The Lancet

Frequency of Solvent Abuse
It is not sufficient to know merely that an individual is involved in solvent abuse since it is essential to be informed of the exact nature and frequency of the involvement if an appropriate treatment and management programme is to be arranged. There was little available information from community groups as to how frequently young people were involved in solvent abuse. The acute

incidents which alerted the police to the practice were those involving violent behaviour, accidents or thefts. Other community groups such as school teachers only became involved in relation to medical symptoms such as intoxication or coma.

Of the 84 Lanarkshire sniffers seen in 1975, 23 per cent had experimented on one to three occasions only and had then stopped. A further 35 per cent had been regularly involved from one to four times per month, 40 per cent were involved more frequently with anything between two and six sessions per week and 2 per cent were involved daily. Similar ranges of frequency were found among 134 children seen at the East End clinic in Glasgow during 1978/79 (see Figure 3.3) although a larger proportion (36 per cent) had tried it on only one to three occasions and 10 per cent were involved daily.

Figure 3.3: Frequency of Solvent Abuse in 134 Cases

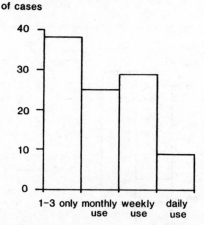

A survey of the extent and frequency of solvent abuse was carried out in a comprehensive school in Glasgow in September 1976.[23] The results indicated that, of the 10 per cent who admitted to sniffing glue, 50 per cent had tried it once only and 21 per cent claimed that they indulged regularly although the term 'regularly' was not clearly defined.

Among those who indulge in solvent abuse on a regular basis, there are wide variations in the frequency of involvement. The study of 55 young people who had been involved for at least ten months, revealed that the frequency of indulgence varied from twice per week (5 per cent) to the use of solvents two or three times per day (40 per cent).

Duration of Solvent Abuse
The length of time during which the young people were involved in solvent abuse shows a wide variation. In Lanarkshire, 77 per cent of a sample of 84 sniffers had been inhaling solvents intermittently for a period of one month to four years with 10 per cent of them being involved for 18 months or longer. Of 134 attending the clinic in the East End ʼof Glasgow between 1978 and 1979, the duration of involvement varied from less than one month (24 per cent) to more than 18 months (4 per cent). Some admitted to as long as five years of involvement. This is demonstrated in Figure 3.4. The study of habitual abusers in Glasgow indicated a duration of involvement which varied between ten months and seven years.

Figure 3.4: Duration of Solvent Abuse in 134 Cases

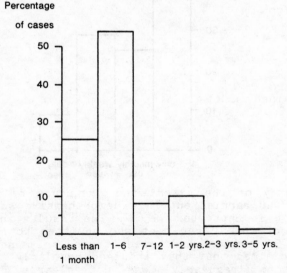

Length of Sessions
When the 84 Lanarkshire sniffers were asked about the length of their sniffing sessions, most (44 per cent) said that they had been involved only briefly

at any one time and certainly for less than 30 minutes, 23 per cent were involved for 30 to 90 minutes, 26 per cent thought that the duration of sessions was from 90 minutes to 3 hours and 7 per cent estimated it to be more than 3 hours. These results, while interesting at the time, were definitely suspect because the children, when intoxicated, really had no clear idea about time and were quite unable to estimate it with any accuracy. The same applied to chronic sniffers whose answers such as 'hours' were given without qualification.

## Amount Taken per Session

Childrens' answers to questions about the amount of substances required for a sniffing session were often vague. Considering the group nature of the activity and the fact that they shared around the tubes, cans and bottles of substances, it would have been difficult if not impossible for them to estimate how much they had taken. For example, if one pint of adhesive is divided up among ten individuals and some indulge to a greater extent than others, it is impossible to work out accurately the dose taken per person during that session.

On the other hand, the amount used per session was well known to the 55 habitual sniffers. They needed amounts that varied from one tube of adhesive per session to four pints of adhesive or eight cans of butane per day. The average amount of chemical taken per day was equivalent to that contained in a half pint of adhesive.

## Exposure to Solvent Abuse

There are a number of varying factors which affect the total amount of exposure to volatile solvents. These variables are the length of the period during which solvent abuse takes place, the frequency and length of the sessions and the amount taken per session. It is therefore obvious that the total dose taken by each individual who abuses solvents will vary enormously. It ranges from the negligible amount taken by those involved only once or twice on an experimental basis to the considerable amounts taken by those who have progressed to frequent and even daily use of substances over a prolonged period of time. No satisfactory method of quantifying the exposure to solvent abuse has so

far been devised and yet it is important to have
this information when working out the risk of
health damage or death for any one individual. All
that can be stated clearly is that enormous
variations exist in all the important, relevant
features of solvent abuse. These features are:

1. The duration of the abuse.
2. The frequency of the sessions.
3. The amount and type of substance used per
   session.
4. The length of the sessions.

Each of these is a contributory factor which must
be considered when estimating the total exposure of
any one individual and each one is important in the
assessment of their degree of risk.


The Places
Since most of the cases of solvent abuse have come
to attention in urban areas, it is reasonable to
assume that most of the activity occurs in such
areas. Like everything else about the practice, the
places chosen for sniffing sessions have been found
to vary considerably. In general, they are chosen
with a view to avoiding detection and in some cases
they have proved to be very isolated. Most of the
activity occurs out of doors and every area has its
favourite spots which have included railway yards,
garages, wooded areas of parks, bin areas, sheds
and waste ground. Since many of these places are
well hidden, it is doubtful whether help could be
summoned in time in the event of an emergency.
Other more dangerous sites chosen have included
bridges, the cabs of cranes on building sites and
well concealed caves but these are not necessarily
the kind of places chosen by all solvent abusers.
The individuals who came to attention were mostly
practising in groups and had therefore attracted
attention because of the numbers involved or the
very nature of the group practice which on many
occasions left plenty of evidence of solvent abuse
on the ground (Figure 3.5). What is not known is
the extent to which others were quietly involved at
home and thus avoided detection.
    Children were often prepared to get wet while
involved in sniffing so long as they could remain
undetected and would sometimes sit huddled under
trees with the rain dripping down on them. In other
cases, 'dens' were fitted out with bits of carpet

to make them more comfortable.

Figure 3.5: Signs of Solvent Abuse - Discarded Bags on the Ground

## Extent of Solvent Abuse
There were 526 people known to be involved in solvent abuse in Lanarkshire between 1970 and 1975 with the numbers increasing annually. However, when the data were studied on a district basis, it was found that there were marked variations between one district and another and that, even within one district, there were fluctuations in the extent of solvent abuse from year to year. Overall, the detected extent of solvent abuse was never more than 2 per cent of the young population. It was obvious from these studies that the practice of solvent abuse was, at most, a passing phase in the lives of some young people. That explains some of the difficulties encountered when researching the matter since, to some extent, it was 'here today and gone tomorrow'. The actual extent of the practice of solvent abuse in the juvenile population of Strathclyde is discussed in Chapter 5.

The Practice of Solvent Abuse

Case Reports

Some features of solvent abuse are well illustrated
by case reports.

## Case 1

In June 1973, a head teacher telephoned the local
Community Involvement Branch of the police to
report that one of his pupils had been involved in
solvent abuse in school. A constable from Community
Involvement attended the school and found that the
boy was sluggish, had slurred speech and required
much prompting when questioned. Eventually, the
pupil admitted that he had been intermittently
sniffing shoe conditioner fumes for some months. He
said that he knew from his friends that sniffing
glue was dangerous but he was not aware that other
substances might also be hazardous. This illustrates
one way in which solvent abuse can be detected and
brought to the attention of the police. It also
illustrates how the juvenile information network
functions.

## Case 2

During the summer of 1974, the police were
concerned about an outbreak of solvent abuse in a
rural part of Lanarkshire. Eight teenagers were
involved and this represented a large number in a
small village. Medical intervention was requested
and four were visited during the first week to
assess the situation. It transpired that all eight
teenagers went to school in the nearby town. There
they had heard about solvent abuse, had decided to
try it out for themselves in a group and in the
process had drawn attention to themselves. After
the case history had been taken for each one,
medical examinations were conducted. During the
following week the remaining four were also visited
at home. All were found to have stopped after a
group discussion about the visit during the
previous week. They had decided that it was not
worth continuing and that they should abandon their
sessions.

    Again, this is a good illustration of children
listening to other children and of the powerful
influence of peer group pressure either in starting
or stopping solvent abuse.

Case 3
A pharmacist telephoned the Community Involvement
Branch of the police in Lanarkshire. He said that
he was aware that some adolescents abused
industrial solvents or petrol in order to become
intoxicated and he wondered if other products could
be misused for the same reason. On being told that
this was the case, he went on to describe to the
police officer how a girl, aged between 14 and 15,
had attracted his attention by purchasing twelve
cans of hair spray each day over a period of
several weeks. He had also noticed that she was
always on her own.
    When the crime prevention officers went to the
girl's house to investigate the matter, they
learned that the girl was aged 14 and had not been
in trouble involving any of the agencies. However,
it appeared that she was having problems at home.
Although the underlying reasons were not clear,
there was no doubt at all that there were frequent
quarrels between the various members of the family.
In order to escape this, the girl had started to
spend increasing periods of time in her room
inhaling the vapours from the cans of hair spray.
She admitted to spending hours each day involved in
this practice because it made her feel better. This
girl and indeed her entire family were found to be
suffering from severe emotional disturbances. After
a large amount of support from the Social Work
Department and considerable psychiatric help, the
girl recovered.
    This is a good example of the solitary and
disturbed abusers and illustrates the difficulties
that may be involved in their detection. In this
case, the girl came to the attention of the
shopkeeper who thought that her behaviour in
purchasing large amounts of hair spray was most
unusual.


Case 4
In 1974 in one part of Lanarkshire, it became
fashionable to add Steradent tablets (non-intoxicating)
to dry-cleaning fluid to increase the rate of
vaporisation and thus to ensure a quick effect when
sniffing from the tops of the bottles. This method
attracted a number of followers although it never
became popular in a widespread way. Information is
inclined to become garbled in transit and somewhere
along the line the details about adding Steradent
tablets to dry-cleaning fluid was lost as the

following rather amusing incident illustrates.

Community Involvement personnel were asked to attend a large comprehensive school in Lanarkshire to help the head teacher investigate an unusual disturbance. Eight boys had been discovered by a teacher in one of the classrooms. They had been coughing and spluttering so much that the noise had drawn attention to the group. What had actually happened was that one boy had told the others of a rumour that if they popped Steradent tablets into their noses and took twelve deep breaths they would see things that no-one else could see. He then produced some Steradent tablets for them to 'have a go'. Naturally, they came to no harm despite prolonged coughing and spluttering. All that they 'saw' to support the rumour was the head teacher's unamused expression and then the faces of the Community Involvement Branch personnel. That seemed to have a salutary effect since none of them came to any attention again.

This case illustrates very clearly the group nature of the activity and shows how misinformation as well as information is passed along the juvenile grapevine.

Case 5

Habitual sniffers very often have a favourite place or den where they can indulge in undisturbed sniffing sessions. One such group used a spot about one mile from the nearest house which could only be reached by climbing many fences, walking through tangled undergrowth beneath trees and finally by climbing down a steep slope into a concealed cave. To say that it was very difficult to find the place in daylight is an understatement and, in darkness, it would have been impossible. The boys in this group, aged from 15 to 17 years, were very experienced sniffers and liked this place because they felt sure that they would never be discovered during their daily sessions. In the event of an emergency, it would have been virtually impossible to summon help quickly.

This case illustrates not only the secretive nature of solvent abuse but also the hazards which sniffers are prepared to ignore in order to find a suitable isolated spot for their sessions.

## Case 6

One very wet Saturday afternoon, the police
discovered a group of four youths sitting beneath
trees passing a bottle of fluid around from one to
the other. They were sniffing from the top of the
bottle, seemed to be very relaxed, happy and quite
unaware that they were already very wet. The bottle
was unlabelled and its contents were not known to
the boys. There was no doubt that the various
members of the group were mildly intoxicated but
not greatly impaired. Subsequent analysis of the
contents of the bottle showed that it contained a
volatile intoxicating solvent.

This is a good example of how young people
learn about different substances which give off
intoxicating vapours and how they experiment with
these effects in groups.

## Case 7

A boy of 14 who was a solitary sniffer used to
indulge his habit mainly in the open air and
usually on waste ground near to his home. From time
to time, he was seen staggering about and on such
occasions had been taken home by the police.

One day, he went off to sniff at the railway
bridge close to his home. He climbed on to the
bridge, sat down, poured the adhesive from a tin
into a small potato crisp bag and applied the bag
to his face. He continued to inhale the vapours for
some time becoming gradually more and more
intoxicated until he eventually lost his balance
and fell from the bridge on to the electrified
railway line beneath. Fortunately, he did not die
but he was severely injured.

This report demonstrates that the risk of
accidents is inherent in the practice of solvent
abuse and that the sites chosen by sniffers can
greatly increase the risk factor in some cases.

## Case 8

Two teenagers were indulging in a sniffing session
in a disused tunnel when it collapsed, burying them
under rubble. The emergency services arrived and,
at one point, it was thought that it might be
necessary to amputate a limb in order to free one
of the boys. Once cutting gear was brought by the
Fire Service, it was possible to remove the boy
from the debris without carrying out an emergency
amputation. Later, one of the boys had a finger

amputated but the outcome could clearly have been much more serious for both.

Again, this illustrates the dangerous places that may be chosen for sniffing.

## Case 9

In 1974, a 15 year-old boy, who did not have a history of regular solvent abuse, decided to go up into a tree with his bag and glue. Once he had climbed the tree, he started to inhale the vapours from the glue until he became very intoxicated. He then lost his balance and fell out of the tree on to his outstretched hands but unfortunately, he fell on to broken glass on the ground below. Both his hands were so badly gashed that he was intermittently hospitalised for some months while undergoing treatment for these injuries.

## Conclusions

When solvent abuse was first mentioned by the Lanarkshire police in 1970, it was not clear which substances were involved, what methods were being used or what proportion of young people were participating in the practice. Since then, information has been gathered from a wide variety of sources, from professional people who are dealing with individual cases and from studies involving large numbers of abusers. The accumulated data have made it possible to describe the characteristics of the practice in some parts of Scotland between 1970 and 1984.

Various terms have been used to describe the practice but within the context of this book, the term solvent abuse has been used. The range of substances which have been abused because of their intoxicating vapours has also been wide, starting with solvents stolen from industrial premises, to rubber cement and paint thinners stolen from garages, adhesives and household cleaning agents bought from shops, and much more recently, aerosols and butane gas. The substances were chosen because of their availability so that, as one substance became unavailable, another was found to take its place.

The methods used to increase the intoxicating effects of inhalation have also varied from time to time and from place to place but these have tended latterly to become more sophisticated and sometimes more dangerous.

The extent of individual involvement has ranged from the occasional sniffing episode to habitual long-term and frequent use. There have also been great variations in the frequency of involvement, duration of involvement, length of sniffing sessions and amount of substance used per session. This makes it difficult, if not impossible, to estimate the cumulative dose of chemical to which any individual has been exposed during the involvement.

Sources of information about solvent abuse for those being initiated were mainly friends at school or living locally. Most solvent abuse episodes appear to have taken place in groups and solitary sniffing was unusual among the solvent abusers who were studied. The fact that it is largely a group activity may have been one of the factors that first attracted attention to solvent abuse and it may also have provided some protection for the abusers themselves.

In view of the enormous range of substances involved, the different methods of inhalation used, the many variations in the sites chosen for sniffing sessions and the individual differences in exposure, it is obvious that the term 'solvent abuse' in itself gives no clue as to the extent of the problem except in a general sense. Only by obtaining accurate and detailed information on an individual basis is it possible to evaluate risk factors and devise appropriate management strategies for each young person involved. However, in the main, solvent abuse represented a short experimental phase in the lives of some young people.

REFERENCES

1. Durden, W.D. and Chipman, D.W. (1967), 'Gasoline sniffing complicated by acute carbon tetrachloride poisoning', <u>Archives of Internal Medicine</u>, <u>119</u>(4), 371-4.
2. Korobkin, R., Asbury, A.K., Sumner, A.J., Nielsen, S.L. (1975), 'Glue sniffing neuropathy', <u>Archives of Neurology</u>, <u>32</u>, 158-62.
3. Press, E. and Done, A.K. (1967), 'Solvent sniffing', <u>Paediatrics</u>, <u>39</u>(4), 451-61 and 611-22.
4. Chapel, J.L. and Taylor, D.W. (1970), 'Drugs for kicks', <u>Crime and Delinquency</u>, <u>16</u>(1), 1-35.
5. Gellman, V. (1968), 'Glue sniffing among Winnipeg school children', <u>Canadian Medical Association Journal</u>, <u>98</u>,411-13.
6. Harris, J.R. (1974), 'A participant observer study: the everyday life of delinquent boys', <u>Adolescence</u>, <u>9</u>(33), 31-48.
7. Cohen, S. (1975), 'Glue sniffing', <u>Journal of the American Medical Association</u>, <u>231</u>(6), 653-4.
8. Wyse, D.G. (1973), 'Deliberate inhalation of volatile hydrocarbons: a review', <u>Canadian Medical Association Journal</u>, <u>108</u>, 71-4.
9. Ackerly, W.C. and Gibson, G. (1964), 'Lighter fluid "sniffing"', <u>American Journal of Psychiatry</u>, <u>120</u>, 1056-61.
10. Sterling, J.W. (1964), 'A comparative examination of two modes of intoxication - an exploratory study of glue sniffing', <u>Journal of Criminal Law, Criminology and Police Sciences</u>, <u>55</u>(1), 94-9.
11. Ellison, W.S. (1965), 'Portrait of a glue sniffer', <u>Crime and Delinquency</u>, <u>11</u>, 394-9.
12. Powars, D. (1965), 'Aplastic anaemia secondary to glue sniffing', <u>New England Journal of Medicine</u>, <u>273</u>(13), 700-2.
13. Wallace, P. (1967), 'A perspective', <u>Juvenile Court Judges Journal</u>, <u>18</u>(2), 44-5.
14. Gregg, M. (1971), 'A note on solvent sniffing in Toronto', <u>Addictions</u>, <u>18</u>, 39-44.
15. Barman, M.L., Sigel, N.B., Beedle, D.B. and Larson, R.K. (1964), 'Acute and chronic effects of glue sniffing', <u>California Medicine</u>, <u>100</u>, 19-22.
16. Dodds, J. and Santostefano, S. (1964), 'A comparison of the cognitive functioning of glue sniffers and non sniffers', <u>Journal of Paediatrics</u>, <u>64</u>(4), 565-70.

17. Massengale, O.N., Glaser, H.H., Le Lievre, R.E., Dodds, J.B. and Klock, M.E. (1963), 'Physical and psychologic factors in glue sniffing', New England Journal of Medicine, 269(25), 1340-4.

18. Watson, J.M. (1977), Solvent Abuse, M.D. Thesis, University of Glasgow.

19. Watson, J.M. (1982), 'Solvent abuse: presentation and clinical diagnosis', Human Toxicology, 1(3), 249-56.

20. Sourindhrin, I. and Baird, J.A. (1984), 'Management of solvent misuse: a Glasgow community approach', British Journal of Addiction, 79, 227-32.

21. Watson, J.M. (1979), 'Solvent abuse: a retrospective study', Community Medicine, 1, 153-6.

22. Oliver, J.S. and Watson, J.M. (1977), 'Abuse of solvents "for kicks": a review of 50 cases', The Lancet, 1(8002), 84-6.

23. Ramsay, A.W. (1982), 'Solvent abuse: an educational perspective', Human Toxicology, 1(3), 265-70

Chapter Four

THE SNIFFERS

It is essential when considering the subject of
solvent abuse to collect as much detailed
information as possible about the practice. So far,
the details presented have concerned the substances
involved, their solvents, the methods of abuse and
the patterns of abuse. A wide variety of
substances, solvents, methods and patterns of abuse
have been described in the world literature since
the 1960s and a similar range has been found in
Strathclyde. It is now necessary to look at the
people who were involved in the practice of solvent
abuse. In particular, it is relevant to describe
the reasons for and the extent of their involvement.


World Profile of Solvent Abusers

It appeared from the literature that people abusing
solvents formed a more discrete group than those
who were involved with other kinds of drugs,
including alcohol. A variety of age ranges have
been quoted in different American studies. Ranges
of 7-17 years, 8-18 years, 12-16 years, 13-17
years, and 9-17 years have been recorded.[1,2,3,4,5]
Although there is some variation in the age ranges
recorded, all are consistent with the conclusion
that solvent abuse is mainly an adolescent
activity.
        Sniffers in America frequently came to the
attention of the law enforcement agencies because
of disruptive behaviour associated with the
practice. There is a preponderance of males over
females in the cases recorded and this is thought
to reflect the nature of the agency involved. For
example, the police would be more likely to observe
large groups of males who were behaving in a

54

disorderly manner. The sex ratios quoted in American studies have ranged from 6:1 to 20:1, for males to females[6],[7],[8] but, as remarked earlier, this may be a reflection of the referral pattern in America. In Canada, the age range and sex ratio were found to be similar.[9] In America, Canada, Sweden and elsewhere, the practice was said to involve groups of deviant teenage males of whom the majority lived in urban areas. It was not always clear from the recorded details whether solvent abuse caused delinquency or whether it occurred more commonly among deviant teenagers.

The practice of solvent abuse was said to have grown from the time that it was first detected and was reported as constituting a numerically large problem in some communities. Some of the available literature on the subject mentions that numerous children experiment and soon stop[4] and that only about one-fifth of adolescents who dabble with solvents later became regular users.[1] Other authors stated that normal middle-class children had been involved but had never come to the attention of the authorities.

Some authors in America and Canada stated quite clearly that there was more than one type of sniffer. In a study of 600 adolescents, said to be of low social class, Stybel, Allen and Lewis[10] differentiated between chronic and social solvent abusers and said that they required different treatment programmes. Gregg,[11] in Toronto, described three groups as experimental abusers, heavy social abusers and chronic long-term abusers. Wyse[8] said that there were two types of abusers - normal teenagers who indulged in social sniffing and habitual sniffers. The reasons suggested for this practice were curiosity and social pressure from the peer group which is an important factor in the lives of most teenagers. These were considered to be the reasons for the involvement of those who were indulging in the so-called social solvent abuse. Habitual users on the other hand were said to be avoiding the unhappy truth about themselves or their circumstances and to be changing their perception in a chemical way to avoid unpleasantness. One author said that habitual solvent abusers had personality characteristics similar to those of alcoholics.[12] Another said that habitual juvenile sniffers had disturbed personalities and were suffering from schizophrenia, psychopathy or anxiety-depression.[1] Yet another author said that those who indulged habitually were emotionally insecure.[7]

Truancy was found to be a common occurrence among children before the onset of solvent abuse and many of the cases reported mention anti-social activities of many kinds ranging from the trivial to the very serious. It was not always clear whether the solvent abuse had led to the delinquent acts or whether solvent abuse was practised more commonly by those who behaved in a delinquent fashion. Of twelve cases studied in Texas,[6] all had a history of anti-social activities prior to the onset of their sniffing practice and in a study of 47 glue sniffers referred to the police in Chicago,[5] all had previous criminal offences. From reports such as these, it certainly appeared that glue sniffing was a new phenomenon associated with delinquency but certainly not causing it.

A study was initiated in Santa Clara County, California in 1962 because the community wanted to know about the factors involved in glue sniffing. 48 habitual sniffers who had been referred to the Juvenile Probation Department were studied for one year. These subjects were found to represent one per cent of all juvenile cases and certain group characteristics were found. They had low interest, low motivation, low intelligence and weak personalities. No evidence was found of physical dependence on solvents but there was some evidence of psychological dependence. At the end of the year, they were described as a group of vulnerable young people from deprived areas whose families faced multiple problems. The solvent abuse was said to be symptomatic of a wider range of problems already known to the social agencies. Not only were solvent abusers involved in anti-social activities which first had brought them to the attention of the authorities but they were also said to be frequently excluded or rejected by their peers because of their aggressive and anti-social behaviour.[12]

In addition to the recurring theme described in the literature of aggressive and anti-social behaviour by habitual solvent abusers, there is also a consistent record of home instability. In a study of twelve sniffers in San Antonio, Texas,[6] it was clearly demonstrated that four of the families were beset by multiple problems. Again, in the case of 16 boys studied in Salt Lake City,[4] an absent father was the relevant factor in each instance. Death, divorce, separation or institutionalisation for some reason accounted for five of the absences while, in the remainder of the cases, relationship between father and son was badly impaired.

In a study of 27 sniffers in Denver, 19 were found to have been arrested for glue sniffing and the remainder referred by parents and school authorities. All were seen at an adolescent clinic and all identified as long-term glue sniffers. It was found that only seven of them had both parents living at home and, in thirteen cases, one or both parents were alcoholics. Another study was carried out in 1961 of 28 solvent sniffers and 28 delinquent controls, all of whom were confined in an institution in Colorado. The backgrounds of both groups were characterised by unstable homes and the lack of a father-figure but there was said to be greater family deterioration among the sniffers than among the delinquent controls.[13,14,15]

This family deterioration might have caused the child to turn to his peer group for support and, having done so, he or she might have been required to conform to the expectations of the group to ensure continuing support. This has been suggested as a possible explanation of why so many children abuse solvents.[6,16] Although it appeared from some of the studies that many of the sniffers belonged to the lower socio-economic groups in America,[12,15] this was not found in other studies.[4,17] This gives rise to the speculation that solvent abuse might be just as common among middle-class children.[9,19]

A special survey, exclusively related to glue sniffing, was launched on 1 July 1965 for a period of 18 months by T. Ruben (judge of the Denver Juvenile Court). It was designed to determine what type of person becomes a habitual sniffer, what renders him or her vulnerable and how the situation can be coped with. Judge Ruben concluded that glue sniffing was, in general, a group activity and that the potential sniffer, suffering from failure at home or at school, who looked to his peers for recognition and affection, had to conform to the expectations of the group to maintain their support. He also found that sniffing was associated with a high rate of truancy and with poor scholastic performance.[18]

Although the degree of involvement with solvents differs considerably from person to person, it was stated by several authors that those individuals who had habitually sniffed glue or other substances would in time graduate from that habit to the abuse of alcohol or drugs. Little information is available about the length of time

involved in the switch from solvent abuse to drug
or alcohol abuse, or about the age of the
individuals concerned. However, in a follow-up
study of 468 cases of glue sniffing commenced in
New York in 1963, 34, most of whom were under
sixteen, were found to have transferred to
narcotics.

Again, in 1970, a study of 47 opiate addicts,
aged 16-43, in Delaware, showed that almost half of
the cases seen had originally experimented with
glue sniffing. In a study of 133 male heroin
addicts in treatment centres in New York between
1972 and 1974, it was found that 26 per cent had
been involved previously in glue sniffing.[19,20,21]
Indeed, it was stated that the solvent abuse
problem in America had reached epidemic proportions
by the 1960s but had appeared to decline after that
due, perhaps, to the ready availability of more
conventional drugs.


## Sources of Information in Strathclyde

By 1973 various details about the individuals
involved in glue sniffing had appeared in the world
literature. However, little information was
available about the phenomenon in Strathclyde and
no-one knew who might be involved in the practice.
There was a general but ill-defined fear that,
because of the easy access to the substances which
could be abused for their intoxicating vapours, the
'infection' might spread to almost all the young
people in the community. This ready availability of
such substances is a crucial factor but it is also
necessary to have individuals who wish to try out
the effects. Therefore, it was important to
discover what were the characteristics of the
people who indulged in the practice and what were
their reasons for becoming involved. Did it
constitute a problem and if so was it a problem
associated with urban deprivation as had been
suggested by the American experience, or were there
significant differences in the pattern of abuse?
Without a doubt, the phenomenon itself depends not
so much on the substances involved as on the people
who abuse them.

Various studies have been carried out in
Lanarkshire and Glasgow since 1973. In America, the
studies of solvent abuse only pertained to those
habitual sniffers who had been referred to an
agency because of anti-social behaviour. These

represented a small number of people with multiple problems. In Strathclyde, solvent abuse has been studied using much larger numbers than those in the American studies and has sometimes involved control groups in order to make valid comparisons with non-abusers. These have provided information about the characteristics of the people indulging in solvent abuse and also given some details about their reasons for involvement in the practice.

During 1973, a study of police statistics about drug abuse and solvent abuse enabled the age distribution of the two groups to be established and compared.

Between 1 January and 31 July, 1975, 84 individuals who had been abusing solvents were investigated. Most, (60 per cent), were referred by the police, another large group, (30 per cent), were in an assessment centre, some, (8 per cent), were referred by social workers, and the remainder were brought by parents. No access to normal non-sniffing children was permitted to prevent a possible spread of the infection. Instead, a control group of 84 young people was selected from the residents of an assessment centre. These individuals, who had never been involved in solvent abuse, were matched on an individual basis for age, sex and home district with the solvent abusers. Much detailed information was collected from the abusers concerning the factors leading to their starting, continuing and stopping the practice and from the non-sniffing control group about their reasons for not being involved. Information was obtained from both groups about their home circumstances, social background, peer groups, hobbies, truancy and anti-social activities.

Starting in 1975, a retrospective study was made of 102 individuals who had been referred, because of solvent abuse, to the Community Involvement Branch of the police between May 1971 and December 1973. A control group of 102 non-sniffers was carefully selected from 650 young people who had also been seen by police personnel between the same dates and who had been warned, but not charged, about anti-social activities such as malicious mischief, breach of the peace or shoplifting. The two groups were matched on an individual basis for age, sex and place of residence. Information was elicited about whether the solvent abusers had been involved in anti-social activities before or after their involvement in solvent abuse. Both groups were studied to determine what proportion of each had indulged in drug or alcohol abuse by 1975.

A study of 18 habitual solvent abusers living in urban areas of Lanarkshire or Glasgow was carried out in 1976. Three groups of six abusers were chosen. The first group consisted of six individuals who had attended a forensic psychiatry centre solely on account of glue sniffing or glue sniffing associated with theft. The second was a random sample of six from 42 habitual sniffers who had been seen by the police solely on account of their glue sniffing activities. Thirdly, a random sample of six was chosen from 20 young males who were admitted to an assessment centre on account of anti-social activities. All 18 had abused glue solvents regularly over a period of at least six months. The purpose of the study was to determine the characteristics of those who habitually abused solvents and to find out to what extent they had subsequently become involved in drug or alcohol abuse.

In October 1976 a study was conducted to define the extent of solvent abuse among 898 pupils attending a secondary school in the East End of Glasgow. This was repeated in 1979 and 1982. Although the study was primarily concerned with establishing the extent of the practice in that area at that particular time, useful information was also obtained about the age range of those who admitted to solvent abuse.

During 1976 and the first four months of 1977, 32 cases of solvent abuse were referred to a psychiatric clinic in the East End of Glasgow. By defining habitual solvent abuse as regular abuse for a minimum period of three months, it was found that 29 of these cases met the requirements of habitual abusers and were studied. These referrals came from a variety of sources. Almost half (45 per cent) came from general practitioners. The remainder came from the accident and emergency department of the local district hospital (10 per cent), from social work departments, (14 per cent), from the courts (10 per cent) and from the local school health co-ordinator (21 per cent).

In 1976, the British Medical Association Brackenbury Award made it possible for the author to set up a screening clinic for one year in the East End of Glasgow in order to study the characteristics of solvent abuse there. It was also intended to provide a service for all those who attended, in matters involving health education and

counselling for parents and children. Individuals
were screened for signs of physical damage and
offered appropriate treatment. It was also possible
to refer appropriate cases to psychiatric clinics,
social agencies and so on. The clinic was held in
the police surgeon's room of a police station,
partly because the police offered the facility for
that purpose, and partly because all other agencies
at that time considered that solvent abuse clinics
should be sited 'elsewhere'. By the end of a year,
134 individuals had attended voluntarily with their
parents and much valuable information had been
obtained. The East End clinic continued to function
after the first year and has since been staffed by
psychiatrists and Community Involvement personnel
from the police, each with a separate remit. It has
continued to provide useful information about
solvent abuse from individuals attending the
clinic. In 1980 a total of 166 cases were seen.

A study by the author of the presentation
patterns of 400 solvent abusers between 1975 and
1981 provided some information on the social
background to some cases. Finally, 55 habitual
abusers of solvents were seen between 1981 and 1984
having been referred to the author by social
workers, youth workers, residential care staff,
psychologists, psychiatrists, health visitors and
general practitioners. A background report was
often sent with the referral giving much information
about the social and family circumstances of
solvent abusers and more information was volunteered
in some cases by the individuals concerned.
Although these studies have contributed their share
towards building up fuller information about those
who abuse solvents, their limitation must be
accepted. The studies themselves have been
completed in different districts at different
times. What may be typical of one district may not
apply in another. Presentations may vary greatly
from time to time and from place to place and so
may the associated problems. In particular, none of
these studies gives any information about solvent
abusers who had not yet come to light and any
comments on a population not yet investigated could
only be speculative at best.

A great deal of information about solvent
abuse and the related group dynamics was obtained
by the author over a period of years as a result of
many interviews with both individuals and groups.
It is worth noting that these individuals were seen
in a variety of different settings such as schools,

police stations, social work offices, clinics,
hospital outpatient departments, health centres,
assessment centres and, sometimes, their own homes.
The information which was collected is described
later in this book.


Results in Strathclyde


Drug Abuse and Solvent Abuse
During 1973 in Lanarkshire, 44 persons had been
found guilty of drugs offences and 69 solvent
abusers had been detected by the police. When the
age distributions of these two groups were compared
it was found that the ages of the drug offenders
ranged from 16-36 years, with an average age of
20,(Figure 4.1) while that for solvent abusers was
9-17 years with an average age of 13 (Figure 4.2).
This indicates clearly that solvent abusers form a
distinct group from the rest of the drug abusers
and their characteristics should be considered
separately. It is with these characteristics that
we are now concerned.


Figure 4.1: Age Distribution of 44 Police Cases of Drug Abuse
in Lanarkshire 1973

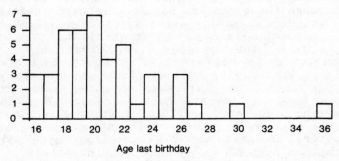

Figure 4.2: Age Distribution of 69 Police Cases of Solvent Abuse in Lanarkshire 1973

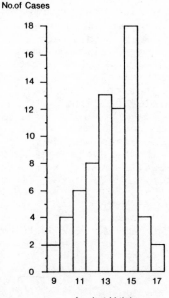

**No.of Cases**

**Age last birthday**

## Age Distribution in Solvent Abuse

The age range found among 102 police cases of solvent abuse in Lanarkshire between 1971 and 1973 was 9-17 years with a mean age of 13.8 years.[22] The age range of 84 cases seen in Lanarkshire in 1975 was 8-16 years with an average age of 13.8 years. In the 1976 survey carried out in the East End of Glasgow, the age range was found to be 11-15 years with most cases lying between 13 and 15 years. Similar results were found when the survey was repeated in 1979 and 1982.[23] Among 29 habitual abusers of solvents attending a psychiatric clinic in the East End of Glasgow between 1976 and 1977, the age range was found to be 10-17 years with an average of 14.5 years.[24] This higher average age may be due to the longer involvement with solvent abuse found among these habitual users.

At the East End clinic, the age range for 134 sniffers seen in 1979 was 9-17 years with an average age of 13.5 years.[25] For 400 solvent abusers seen between 1975 and 1981, the age range was 8-19 years, most being between 13 and 15 years. A study of 55 habitual sniffers from the northern part of Glasgow between 1981 and 1984 gave an age range of 8-28 years with an average age of 14.7 years.

Although these studies were carried out at different times and in different places among different people in different situations and although they were carried out by different investigators, the results are remarkably consistent. There is much less variation in the age distribution than might have been expected. The average remained fairly constant between 13.5 and 13.8 years except in the cases of the habitual sniffers who, by definition, had been involved for longer than the average abuser and were therefore older. The average in these cases was between 14.5 and 14.7 years. The age at which the peak incidence occurred in all these studies was 13 to 15 years. A typical age distribution of 102 cases is given in Figure 4.3.

Figure 4.3: Typcial Age and Sex Distribution of Cases of Solvent Abuse

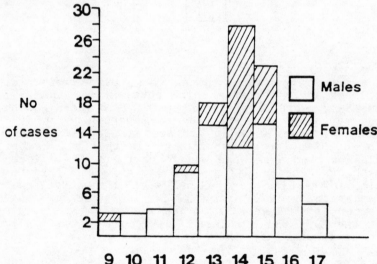

In those studies which contained female abusers the average age was 0.5 years older except for the study of 55 habitual sniffers in which the females were 0.5 years younger. However, the number of females was relatively small and these results may merely be caused by random fluctuations which can occur in a small sample.

## Sex Distribution in Solvent Abuse

In the study of police cases seen from 1971 to 1973 the ratio of males to females was found to be 2:1. It was 8.3:1 in the 84 cases in Lanarkshire in 1975. The school survey involved an all male school. The cases seen at the psychiatry clinic in the East End of Glasgow were all male. Of the 134 who attended the East End police clinic during 1979, males outnumbered the females by 4.4 to 1. The ratio among the 400 solvent abusers seen in Glasgow was 4.8:1 and among the 55 habitual abusers in Glasgow it was 5:1.

A possible explanation for the large numbers of males is that boys are more likely than girls to be involved in groups and because of this to attract greater attention. However, this fails to explain why the sex ratio was only 2:1 in the police cases seen between 1971 and 1975, while in the cases referred by general practitioners, psychologists and others, the ratio was 5:1. If the argument is that group activities cause a higher detection rate, then the police figures would be expected to show a higher proportion of males. Another explanation might be that males, in general, are more likely than females to experiment with intoxicants and hence are more likely to be involved in solvent abuse. There is also the possibility that, since the intoxication from the abuse of solvents reduces control over behaviour, boys would be more likely to indulge in aggressive behaviour which would be noticed. Whatever the explanation, it is clear that solvent abuse appears to be a phenomenon which involves mainly young teenage males aged between 13 and 15 years.

## Urban Areas

In America, most of the literature mentions that the prevalence of solvent abuse is higher in urban areas. In the study of 102 police cases in Lanarkshire, 90 per cent of the individuals lived in urban areas and this was particularly true of the girls for it was found that only one of 29 girls lived in a rural area. In the Lanarkshire study of 84 cases in 1975, 91 per cent lived in urban areas, the remainder in rural areas.

In all the studies carried out in the East End of Glasgow, the children lived in urban areas and this was also so in the study of 55 habitual sniffers from the north of Glasgow. However, in the study of 400 clinically presented cases, 2 per cent of those seen came from prosperous suburban areas.

<u>Social Class</u>
Much of the literature about solvent abuse
suggests, if it does not actually state, that
solvent abuse is typically, or even exclusively, a
practice of the deprived or delinquent. It has
sometimes been implied that all solvent sniffers
belong to social class V. (The Registrar General's
classification of occupation ranges from social
class I to social class V and is described in Table
4.1).

Table 4.1: The Registrar General's Social Class Categories

|  | Type of occupation | Examples |
|---|---|---|
| Social Class I | Professional occupations | Doctors, physicists, veterinary surgeons |
| Social Class II | Intermediate occupations | Journalists, farmers, musicians |
| Social Class III N | Skilled non-manual occupations | Secretaries, photographers, draughtsmen |
| M | Skilled manual occupations | Printers, joiners, chefs |
| Social Class IV | Partly skilled occupations | Roofers, glaziers, storekeepers |
| Social Class V | Unskilled occupations | Dockers, porters, window cleaners |

However, studies in Strathclyde have shown
otherwise. In the study of 84 individuals in
Lanarkshire, the occupation of the father was
assigned to a social class using the 1970

'Classification of Occupations'. The result showed that no children from social class I were present in the sample but that all other social classes were represented, with 2 per cent from social class II, 41 per cent from social class III, 25 per cent from social class IV and 32 per cent from social class V. This represents a very wide social class distribution. In a study of 18 habitual sniffers, social classes II to V were again represented with 5 per cent, 39 per cent, 39 per cent and 17 per cent respectively. In the study of 400 solvent abusers in Glasgow, 2 per cent were from social class I with the remainder giving a normal distribution in social classes II to V.[27]

## Home Factors

In the study of 84 abusers in 1975, 83 lived at home with one or both parents and the remaining child lived with grandparents. Enquiry into whether parents were dead, divorced or separated revealed that 76 per cent of the sniffers lived at home with both parents. In 12 per cent of the cases, one or both of the parents were dead and a further 12 per cent of the parents were divorced or separated. Similar results were obtained for the 84 controls with no statistical differences between the two groups.

In the study of 134 cases in the east end of Glasgow, it was found that 61 per cent of the children lived at home with both parents. In 9 per cent of the cases, one or both parents were dead and 30 per cent of the parents were separated or divorced. Thus 39 per cent of the children lived in a one-parent family. When this was compared with a group of 100 non-sniffing children from local schools, it was found that 83 per cent of them lived at home with both parents and only 17 per cent were from one-parent families.[26]

Therefore it can be concluded from these figures that children from one-parent families are more likely to become solvent abusers than those where both parents are present.

In the study of 55 habitual users, 33 per cent were in residential care and a further 11 per cent were said to have multiple problems of one kind or another at home.

It is obvious that there is a wide range of home circumstances among those who abuse solvents so that no one pattern is true for all. It would certainly not be true to state that solvent abuse per se led to the behaviour which then required the residential care described, nor is it valid to claim that it led to the multiple problems present in these cases. However, it may well have accentuated existing problems. What would be true to say is that solvent abuse seems to occur more commonly among people who have other difficulties in their lives.


## Paternal Employment

In the Lanarkshire study of 1975, six of the fathers were dead, a large proportion of the remainder were employed (72 per cent) and the rest were out of work for one reason or another. In the control group, 64 per cent of the fathers were employed and there was therefore no significant difference between the two groups in respect of paternal employment.

However, in the East End of Glasgow, it was found that, of the 134 who attended the clinic, 51 per cent had fathers who were unemployed and this compared markedly and unfavourably with the control group where only 23 per cent of the fathers were unemployed and with the average unemployment rate for the East End which was 20%. These figures are statistically significant and suggest an association between paternal unemployment and solvent abuse. However, it is not valid to imply from this that unemployment is the cause and solvent abuse is the effect.


## Maternal Employment

In 4 of the 84 Lanarkshire cases, the mother was dead. Of the remaining 80 cases, 58 per cent of the mothers were housewives and did not work outside the home. In 66 per cent of the 134 cases attending the East End clinic, the mothers were housewives and did not work outside the home. In some of the chronic, habitual cases, the mothers had never worked outside the home and were excellent homemakers.


## Parental Alcohol Problems

Although parental alcohol problems are frequently described in the American studies as a factor in solvent abuse, it has been very difficult to gather much detailed information on that subject in Strathclyde. However, parental drunkenness was seen to occur on occasions during visits by the author in Lanarkshire from 1973 to 1975.

In the survey of 84 Lanarkshire solvent abusers seen in 1975, 50 per cent volunteered the information that their fathers were sometimes drunk. This compared unfavourably with 32 per cent in the control cases. Also, 25 per cent of the mothers of the sniffers were said to have got drunk as compared with 5 per cent of the mothers of the controls. As in the American studies, there would thus seem to be an association between alcohol abuse in some parents and solvent abuse in their children but no details were available from the study about what the children considered as 'drunk' or how often this state was reached.

Parental drunkenness, particularly among fathers, has been noted by the author over the years in various clinical situations involving children who abuse solvents. Again, there was no way of establishing the extent to which alcohol problems existed within the family or, even if that were known, what connection, if any, it might have on the children's solvent abuse.

Later studies gave similar results. In the study of 32 habitual sniffers attending a psychiatric clinic in the East End of Glasgow, 59 per cent had parents or step-parents with a known problem of alcohol abuse. The information given by 55 habitual sniffers seen in Glasgow between 1981 and 1984 indicated that there was an alcohol problem in respect of one parent in ten of the cases and in one case both parents were alcoholics.

There has never been a definite statement in the literature that children of problem drinkers would sniff glue but, if there is any correlation, it would surely be because, all too often, children are merely imitating their parents and turning to a readily available intoxicant to help them cope with their problems.


## The Age of Commencement of Solvent Abuse

The age at which children first become involved in solvent abuse is an important part of any description of the problem. When the 84 Lanarkshire sniffers were asked about the age at which they started, a varying response was obtained, from 8-16 years with the average at 12.9 years. As these were significantly lower than the ages of the children at the time of referral, it suggested a long history of solvent abuse in at least some of the cases.

In the East End study, the starting ages varied between 7 and 16 years with an average of 13.2 years. Again, these values reflect a long history of solvent abuse in some cases.

In the study of 55 chronic cases, the ages of starting were found to range between 7 and 26 years with a mean at 13 years. Once again, the difference between these ages and the ages of the same individuals at the time of presentation represented a lengthy history of solvent abuse in all cases.

Knowledge and Experience of Solvent Abuse

It was considered to be very important to find out from the children involved in solvent abuse how they had first heard about it and why they had become involved. The information obtained in this way is more authentic and more useful than any explanations that might be argued from some theoretical basis.

Accordingly, the 84 Lanarkshire children were asked for their sources of information about solvent abuse and these turned out to be mostly friends, some of whom lived locally (56 per cent), some at school (35 per cent), older siblings (2 per cent) and 'others seen sniffing'. One child said that he had read about it in the newspapers and wanted to try it.

When the 84 controls, who had never abused solvents, were asked the same question, 30 per cent stated that they had never heard about the practice and, indeed, in answer to the question about 'sniffing' some responded with remarks like 'you mean like when I have a cold?'. The remaining 70 per cent had heard about solvent abuse, solvent sniffing, glue sniffing and so on. Their main sources of information were school friends (39 per cent), friends living locally (13 per cent) and friends they had made in residential establishments (14 per cent). Older siblings contributed only 2 per cent of the sources and one child said that he first learned of the practice by watching a group of children indulging. Each of these individuals voluntarily gave the names of others who had been involved in solvent abuse and this group represented in each case 10 to 15 children who had not been identified as abusers.

The control cases were asked why they had not become involved. The main reasons given were that their friends did not do it (25 per cent), that they regarded it as stupid (25 per cent) or because they thought that it might damage their health (50 per cent). The damage to health which they anticipated included general damage, brain damage ('It would rot your brains') and death.

The reasons given by the test group for their involvement in the practice varied. Most (70 per cent) said that they indulged because their friends did it and they were anxious not to be left out. Others (26 per cent) said that they started because they wanted to try for themselves a practice that they had only heard about from other people. One girl said that she had turned to solvent abuse because it was a cheap substitute for alcohol. She would have preferred to drink and, indeed, claimed that she sometimes had as much as a quarter bottle of vodka two or three times per week. However, when she was short of money, sniffing toluene fumes from glue provided a reasonably cheap, if not entirely satisfactory alternative. The remaining child had heard that it was possible to 'see things' when under the influence of glue fumes and had started the practice in the hope of seeing his mother who had been dead for two years.

The 84 solvent abusers were then asked about their reasons for stopping the practice, this gave some interesting results. Some (31 per cent) had not stopped at all. Of those who had, 33 per cent said that they were following the lead of their friends who had stopped, 14 per cent had stopped after the police had visited their home to express concern about the practice, 12 per cent had stopped because their curiosity had been satisfied, 14 per cent stopped because they were worried about their health and 28 per cent stopped because solvent abuse had made them sick or dizzy. Altogether, 66 per cent of the control group and 67 per cent of the test group believed that there were no possible health hazards associated with solvent abuse. The remaining 23 per cent of the control group believed that brain damage, general physical deterioration, lung damage or addiction might result. All of the test group were well aware of the effects of solvent abuse and quite a number could compare it with the effects of alcohol. Of these, many said that they would have preferred alcohol if it had been available.

It is important to note the influence of the peer group in spreading information about the practice of solvent abuse and in initiating the involvement of some children while influencing others not to become involved. Similar peer group influences were found to operate with respect to the smoking and drinking histories of the two groups of 84 individuals. The ages at which both these groups had first experimented with these other practices were almost identical in each case and the reasons given were the same as those for solvent abuse, namely, curiosity and the influence of friends and siblings.

Sometimes there were more obvious demonstrations of the powers of peer group pressure than just verbal confirmation. Tattoos had been noted during clinical examinations on 23 per cent of the sniffers. These were, without exception, self inflicted by using needles or pins to prick particles of Indian ink into the skin (Figure 4.4).

Figure 4.4: Self-inflicted Tattoos

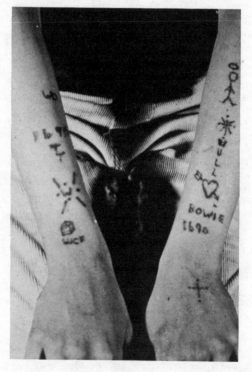

This process had been carried out as a condition of peer group membership and was of vital importance to those concerned. The same situation was found in 30 per cent of the control cases and was again found to be due to peer group pressure.

## Solvent Abuse and the Peer Group

The main determinant in these situations is not simply the peer group itself but the combination of the pressure exerted by the peer group and the vulnerability of the individual. This would determine the extent to which a person was likely to be influenced by peer group pressure into participating in any current peer group fashion such as smoking or drinking. Adolescents are particularly sensitive to peer group influence as they mature from children into adults. A large amount of experimentation occurs during this phase of emotional and physical development and the peer group plays an important role in the experimental process. As individuals mature and draw away from their parents, the peer group becomes more important and may provide them with help and support. In order to ensure the continuing approval and support of his peers, the adolescent will tend to conform to the demands and practices of the group, whatever these might be. The greater the insecurity of the adolescent, the more likely he or she is to require the continuing approval and support of the group.

This was found to be true in relation to solvent abuse. Most individuals, regardless of social background, were involved infrequently in the practice and only to the extent of an 'odd sniff' in order to be like the others or because of curiosity. However, some individuals who were very much in need of group support might be involved in repeated sessions of solvent abuse. Their actual personal involvement might be limited to only small doses which did not increase with time but they needed to be seen to be conforming. When histories were taken from these abusers, the frequency of the sessions was variable but the amount taken was never large and did not increase. These young people showed no behaviour changes and there was no withdrawal from relationships. If the group moved on to some other activity, they moved on too and they never indulged on their own. They were vulnerable because of their need for group support and approval but to them solvent abuse did not become a long-term problem.

A third and smaller group has also been

identified among solvent abusers. The people in it frequently start the practice along with their peer group but, as time passes, they take more and more of the substances in order to achieve the same effect as they had previously obtained from much smaller amounts. Although their solvent abuse had begun as a peer group activity, they continued it long after the peer group had abandoned it and moved on to other activities. These individuals then either started solitary sniffing or joined a group of other chronic sniffers.

Unlike the peer groups, where, by definition, the individuals are the same age and live in the same area or attend the same school, these groups of chronic sniffers are characterised by the fact that they contain individuals who differ in age and who may not live in the same area or attend the same school. The groups exist specifically to indulge in solvent abuse with money and resources being pooled in order to obtain the required substances and the means to sniff them. Individuals take it in turns to buy whatever is required or, if their need for the substances outstrips their resources, they begin to steal from shops. These thefts are often well planned and executed. When indulging in sniffing sessions, these groups often arrange to have a 'look-out man' to spot signs of trouble and to take action in an emergency. Theoretically, this seems to suggest a safety factor but in practice this look-out often ends up as impaired as the others.

Although these individuals represent only about 10 per cent of the known abusers, they are more likely to become unconscious, have accidents or to suffer long-term damage than the rest because their exposure to solvents is of much longer duration, their dose per session is larger and the frequency of sessions is greater. Individually, they often use three or four pints of adhesive or several cans of aerosol during each day. These abusers are not indulging because of social pressures but because of some underlying need to escape from the realities of their lives. This is probably also true of other habitual abusers who are never involved with a group but indulge on their own.

To summarise, there would seem to be three distinct classes of solvent abusers:

1.   The experimental peer group user.
2.   The social peer group user.

### 3. The habitual solvent abusers.

Of all solvent abusers, 30-40 per cent are involved on only a few occasions, 40-50 per cent are involved sporadically with their peer group, over a few weeks or months, and 10 per cent are likely to become habitual sniffers. These categories are not entirely separated since individual sniffers may move from one to another. It is important to identify habitual solvent abuse because such cases will require different management.

The finding of a solitary sniffer usually indicates that the individual concerned is abusing solvents for their chemical effects and not because of social pressure. This person invariably has problems with his relationships at home or with friends, and he or she becomes more isolated as time passes. The problems encountered were wide-ranging and included conflict within the family, much of it pre-dating the solvent abuse; alcoholic parents, single parents unable to cope and other similar reasons which resulted in an unusually turbulent adolescence. In spite of this, it must not be thought that the habitual solitary solvent abuser invariably comes from a background of urban deprivation or has alcoholic and/or uncaring parents. Some of the habitual abusers seen came from middle class suburban homes and many from caring families of whatever social class. However, most lived in areas of multiple deprivation. Individual factors seemed to play an important part in solitary, habitual solvent abuse and it could certainly be said that, in these cases, the solvent abuse represented an individual response to some form of stress. It was certainly clear that habitual solvent abuse was not induced by any feature of the substances themselves but was determined by the people involved. It was equally obvious that, unless their underlying problems could be identified and tackled, solvent abuse was likely to continue, and even if it did stop, it was very likely to be replaced by alcohol or drug abuse.

### Alcohol and Drug Use

The 102 solvent abusers detected by the police in Lanarkshire between 1971 and 1973 were compared in 1975 with the control group for subsequent drug and alcohol use. It was found that six of the solvent abusers had been involved in drug abuse by 1975. In five cases, the drug was cannabis and in one case it was mandrax. Only one of the controls had been involved with drugs in the same period, the drug being cannabis. The numbers in this sample are very small and can only indicate, but not confirm, a possible link between solvent abuse and later drug abuse. There is no evidence that solvent abuse causes subsequent drug abuse. It is much more likely that vulnerable individuals will change readily from one suitable intoxicant to another.

In the study of 84 solvent abusers in 1975, one admitted to smoking cannabis. She was a 16-year-old girl who had experimented with solvents, alcohol and cannabis. None of the other solvent abusers or controls admitted to any involvement with drugs.

When asked about alcohol consumption, 80 per cent of the sniffers and 85 per cent of the controls said that they either never took alcohol at all or only took it occasionally. The remainder in each group admitted to consuming alcohol weekly. The age at which they started was 12-16 years in both groups and they usually drank lager or beer. None of the solvent abusers drank during sniffing sessions.

Of the 134 children seen in the East End police clinic in 1979, only one admitted to drinking during a sniffing session. In the follow up study there was said to be no evidence in the East End of drug abuse having begun with solvent abuse. There has, however, been speculation that solvent abuse may be linked with the abuse of drugs in other parts of Glasgow.

In a study of 18 habitual solvent abusers,[27] there was again no evidence that drug abuse had followed solvent abuse except in three cases where there was a conversion from solvent abuse to heavy drinking. These cases occurred within a period as short as six months and happened at the ages of 12-14 years. In view of family histories characterised by heavy alcohol consumption, it was thought that the onset of heavy drinking would have happened in due course irrespective of the solvent abuse factor.


Truancy
Of the 84 children seen in 1975, 55 per cent had truanted from school but this truancy had pre-dated the start of solvent abuse in many cases. Frequent truancy was certainly a common factor among the 28

76

habitual abusers attending the psychiatric clinic in Glasgow and, in a quarter of these cases, it had begun before the solvent abuse. Among the 55 chronic sniffers attending the clinic in the north of Glasgow, all but two admitted to persistent truancy, and all those who had truanted thought that it had started before they turned to sniffing solvents.

## Anti-social Behaviour

One-third of the 102 cases of solvent abuse recorded by the police in Lanarkshire had been involved in some criminal offence before starting solvent abuse and half of them had been so involved afterwards. In the study of 84 sniffers in Lanarkshire, 42 per cent of them had been involved in some kind of anti-social activity such as theft, breach of the peace or assault but the remaining 58 per cent had never been in any kind of trouble. Criminal offences had been committed by all 28 habitual sniffers attending a psychiatric clinic in Glasgow.[24] Of these, 28 per cent had committed the offence before the onset of solvent abuse and 62 per cent had done so subsequently.

While it would appear that solvent abuse occurred sporadically in some cases during the course of delinquent careers, there were many other cases where there was no overt evidence of deviance. It seems certain that solvent abuse was also practised by some normal young people during adolescence.

## Intelligence and Achievement

In much of the literature, especially that from America, a great deal has been written about the low intelligence, low achievement and low motivation of solvent abusers. None of the several studies of solvent abusers in various parts of Strathclyde contain systematic estimates of intelligence. An IQ was available for only four of the 84 Lanarkshire children seen in 1975, two being over 100 and two under 100. One of the boys, who was actually a habitual sniffer, had an IQ well in excess of 120. Others seen by the author over the years have been clearly intelligent and articulate although their intelligence quotients had not been formally assessed.

The general impression obtained is that many of the children who repeatedly involve themselves in solvent abuse do under-achieve. Sooner or later, they truant from school in order to indulge the habit more frequently and, as a result, they become educationally retarded. Because of this and also because of the lack of drive and energy associated with habitual solvent abuse, these children fall behind their peers at school and, as a consequence, truant even more. In addition, habitual sniffers whose reasons for being involved in the practice are psychological rather than social, become emotionally more distant from their peers as time goes on. This, in turn strengthens the psychological reasons for dependence on solvent abuse and creates a vicious circle which is difficult to break.

The author has certainly seen at least six individuals all of whom were sports captains or school captains and who had therefore been apparently successful before they became habitually involved in solvent abuse. Once that had begun, their performances had deteriorated and they had completely failed to maintain their levels of success. Solvent abuse per se was not the cause of the deterioration since they had all suffered traumatic losses in their lives such as the death of a parent or grandparent.

The author's overwhelming impression of habitual sniffers is one of apathy and lack of motivation. They appear to be totally negative and to lack drive. When these individuals were first seen, it was not clear whether this was a result of habitual abuse of solvents or whether these young people had had the same attitudes before. Their mothers often commented on this apathy and lack of drive as being aspects which developed after the start of solvent abuse and which increased as they became more involved.

There are no statistics on this subject and the factors involved are complicated and difficult to quantify. What is clear however, is that by no means all solvent abusers who were seen were of low intelligence and neither had they all failed to achieve prior to their involvement. Notable features were the apathy and lack of motivation which were seen in the habitual abuser which may be directly attributable to the chronic abuse of solvents.

The Sniffers

Some Case Histories

## Case 1
In 1974, a twelve-year-old boy was brought to the
attention of the Community Involvement Branch of
the police by his father who said that he wanted
some help with the boy because he was 'at his wits
end'. He was aware, he said, that the police took
an interest in the problem of children who abused
solvents and he knew of no-one else who did. The
father, who lived in a village, was a widower whose
wife had died two years previously and left three
children, aged seven, ten and twelve years. He had
found his twelve-year-old boy sniffing the fumes
from a dry-cleaning fluid in his bedroom.
    The personnel from the Community Involvement
Branch paid a visit to the home. They ascertained
that the boy had been sniffing vapours because he
had been told that people saw things if they
sniffed the fumes from dry-cleaner. He desperately
wanted to conjure up a picture of his dead mother
and had tried to do so on a number of occasions
without success. As soon as it was explained to him
that solvent abuse could never help him achieve
this goal and that, in addition, he was upsetting
his family and perhaps risking his health, he
stopped abusing the dry-cleaner. He lived in a
loving home but one in which there had recently
been a lot of grief. Readjustment was proving
difficult for all concerned including the father
who did not like to admit that he was finding it
difficult to cope with his job and be a full-time
single parent at the same time. The family doctor,
the minister and the neighbours were all subsequently
involved in helping this family and, eventually,
everything settled down.
    This is an example of a problem which
presented as solvent abuse but in which the abuse
was merely a symptom of underlying difficulties. It
took very little to stop the solvent abuse but the
basic problems were more complex and took longer to
resolve.


## Case 2
A 15-year-old boy was reported to the Community
Involvement Branch by neighbours. He was frequently
seen to be intoxicated but the cause of his drunken
state was not known to be solvent abuse. The boy
who lived in a deprived urban area had been

79

successful at school, excelling both in work and at sport. He was top of his class, sports captain for his year and was bright, alert and neatly dressed. Although there was a great deal of glue sniffing in the area and among his school companions, he had not been involved until after his grandmother died. The boy, who had always been very attached to his grandmother, became inconsolable, moody and withdrawn. Soon he started to sniff glue, always on his own and for hours at a time. He was seen by the neighbours who became concerned about him. Over a period of twelve months, he became a habitual user of various volatile substances. He stayed away from home, was frequently seen to be intoxicated and his appearance rapidly deteriorated. He was seen by Community Involvement Branch personnel several times and appointments were made for him with his doctor but he always defaulted. Eventually, he did go, was given psychiatric and social work support and finally, after working his way through his grief reaction, he stopped abusing solvents.

This is another case where solvent abuse drew attention to underlying problems, in this case an overwhelming grief reaction to the loss of a much loved family member.


Case 3
A 14-year-old boy was admitted to an assessment centre because of a variety of anti-social activities. After admission, it was discovered that he had been sniffing glue fumes for two years. He had started along with other boys in his area and they had continued to indulge in the practice sporadically for about six months. When the others had stopped sniffing, he had carried on because, in the first place, he liked it, and because he felt better when sniffing than at any other time. As time passed, he found that he required more solvents to achieve the intoxicated effect that he desired and, by the time of his admission to the assessment centre, he was using about four pints of adhesive every day. There were many underlying problems in this case and, although he stopped glue sniffing, he became increasingly delinquent and apparently began to drink very heavily within a few months of leaving the assessment centre.


Case 4
A girl of fourteen was brought by her mother to the

author because of her glue sniffing. She had been involved with a group of girls who had banded together on a few occasions after school and indulged in glue sniffing episodes of short duration and with little effect other than a few giggles. The mother was very alarmed about the implications of this activity.

A simple explanation about the experimental and transitory nature of the activity in this case, along with the normal results of the medical examination which followed, reassured the mother. The concern expressed to the girl by her parents about possible risks to health was sufficient to cause her to stop her involvement in glue sniffing although she was seen several times afterwards at her own request because of problems with acne. For her, like many others, the involvement with solvent abuse was minimal and transitory.

Case 5

A group of boys, aged 11 to 15, were persistently drawn to the attention of the Community Involvement Branch because of their solvent abuse. They experimented with many substances, including rubber cement, dry-cleaning fluid and finally adhesives. They drew attention to themselves by their disruptive behaviour while under the influence of the intoxicating vapours. The number in the group varied between four and twelve with one of the boys, aged 15, from a professional middle-class background, as the apparent ring-leader. Eventually, this boy was arrested for a variety of offences including theft and breach of the peace. He was sent to an assessment centre for a period of time and, while he was away, the group became interested in youth club activities and none of them continued with solvent abuse. By the time the 15-year-old reappeared in the community, his peers were no longer interested in the practice.

This case illustrates the influence which can be wielded by a strong personality on the other members of a group, particularly when he or she is older than the rest.

Case 6

A nine-year-old boy was seen by the author because of his repeated glue sniffing activities near his home in an urban area. He was given a physical examination and found to be well. His mother who

81

was very worried about him said that, since his
father had died six months previously, the boy had
been going out with a group of older boys and had
sometimes been forced to sniff glue fumes when he
was with them. The mother disliked the bad
influence exerted by the older boys on her son and
said that she would send the boy away to spend the
summer with relatives he liked. When the boy
returned in the autumn, he no longer wanted to be
involved with the older boys and made some new
friends of his own age at school.

In this case, the glue sniffing was a
condition of this boy's acceptance into the group.
As the youngest member, he had to do as the others
wished. When he returned home in the autumn, he had
matured a great deal and no longer needed to be
with the older boys since he was able to make
friends of his own age.

## Conclusions

Solvent abuse was originally considered by the
police to be part of the drug abuse pattern
involving adolescents. This was confirmed by
comparison with the age distribution in the 1973
cases of drug and solvent abuse in Lanarkshire when
the average ages of the two groups were found to be
20 and 13 years respectively. The age distribution
for solvent abuse was also found to be very narrow
in comparison with that for drug abuse. All the
studies of solvent abuse in different places at
different times gave 13 to 15 years as the ages for
peak involvement and were remarkably consistent in
this respect.

The sex ratio of males to females varied from
study to study. In some, only males had been
referred or were involved. In others this ratio was
found to vary between 2:1 and 8:1. Two of the
factors involved in this variation were thought to
be peer group activity, whereby males attracted
more attention thus biasing the detection rate, and
secondly the greater likelihood of males rather
than females experimenting with intoxicants.

The majority of people seen in the studies
came from urban areas although, in some, 10 per
cent of the cases were from rural areas. Some lived
in places of great deprivation but 2 per cent of
the young people were found to be from prosperous
suburban homes. Indeed, every kind of home
environment from the very prosperous to the very

poor had been represented in the cases seen. When the information about social class was analysed, it was found that children from every class had been involved in solvent abuse at some time or another.

When the home backgrounds of solvent abusers in the East End of Glasgow were compared with those of other children in the same area, it was found that the abusers were more likely to belong to one-parent families than the controls. However, it was also clear that most solvent abusers lived at home with both parents in the East End study (61 per cent) and in the Lanarkshire study (76 per cent).

Most of the studies indicated that the majority of the fathers of solvent abusers were employed but, in the East End of Glasgow the unemployment rate was higher than that for the fathers of the controls and much higher than the average rate for the district. In most cases, the mothers of solvent abusers did not work outside the home. Thus, one out of three studies which looked at parental employment indicated an association between paternal unemployment and solvent abuse but none showed any association between solvent abuse and working mothers.

The young people gained their knowledge of solvent abuse from the other members of their peer group. Friends at school and those who lived nearby were particularly influential. Peer group pressure and curiosity were the most important reasons for starting and also for stopping. Peer group pressure was also an important influence in the control groups where it had sometimes influenced against starting solvent abuse. The influence of the peer group was also evident in the drinking and smoking histories of some children and in the self-inflicted tattoos seen on some of them.

Three groups of abusers were identified. Firstly, there was the normal experimental peer group user who never became very involved in the practice. Secondly, there was the individual who particularly required peer group approval and the attraction was really the company and support of the rest of the group rather than the effects of the practice. Although this individual would be more involved in solvent abuse than the experimental user, the dose would be low and the duration short. The rate of abuse would not increase and there would be few behaviour changes. The third group is the smallest but the most difficult to treat. It consisted of those who had always indulged alone and those who had continued with solvent abuse after the rest of their peer group had abandoned the practice. The latter either started solitary sniffing or joined a group of other chronic abusers. Members of this group met solely to promote the habit, and took it in turns to provide the necessary substances, by theft if required. They were not all of the same age and might have come from different districts. The amount of substances used increased with time and was sometimes very large. Individuals in this group were likely to have troubled relationships because of their altered behaviour which could be both irritable and aggressive. They frequently truanted from school and became very isolated. Their involvement in solvent abuse was a symptom of some deep underlying problem which should be the real focus of attention.

A number of factors thought to be linked to solvent abuse were found to have no obvious causal association with it. No evidence was found of progession from solvent abuse to alcohol or drug abuse. About half of the children seen in the study had truanted but the truancy had started before the solvent abuse in most cases.

In about 30-40 per cent of the cases, some criminal offences had been committed before the onset of solvent abuse and it was said in these cases that solvent abuse was part of the general pattern of delinquent behaviour. However, this fails to explain why 60 per cent of solvent abusers had never been involved in criminal offences and makes it clear that solvent abuse can occur in non-delinquent children.

There is little documented evidence in Strathclyde about the intelligence and achievement of solvent abusers but the author has seen some individuals who were highly intelligent and who were successful before becoming involved in the practice.

It is obvious that deviant behaviour, urban deprivation, multiple family problems and alcoholic parents are not adequate reasons to offer as explanations for all cases of abuse of solvents by young people. Many of them were not deviant, did not live in deprived areas and came from stable two-parent families. It seems that, in the majority of cases, these were normal children from normal homes who became involved fleetingly in solvent abuse due to curiosity, to chance encounters or to the pressure of friends. The evidence also makes it clear that most children soon abandon the practice.

In a much smaller number of cases, where it was not to be a passing phase, there was great variation in the social circumstances of the children involved. It was necessary, regardless of the social environment, to uncover and treat any underlying problems with which the solvent abuse might be associated. In some cases, the solvent abuse was due to social pressures on an individual who for some reason was particularly susceptible and in the remaining few cases it was due to some psychological problem.

Finally, it is perfectly clear that no single statement can be made to cover all categories of solvent abuse or to fully describe all the individuals who have at times abused solvents for their intoxicating effects.

REFERENCES

1.  Cohen, S. (1973), 'The volatile solvents', Public Health Reviews, 2(2), 185-214.
2.  Corliss, L.M. (1965), 'A review of evidence on glue sniffing - a persistent problem', Journal of School Health, 35, 442-9.
3.  Dodds, J. and Santostefano, S. (1964), 'A comparison of the cognitive functioning of glue sniffers and non sniffers', Journal of Paediatrics, 64(4), 565-70.
4.  Press, E. and Done A.K. (1967), 'Solvent sniffing', Paediatrics, 39(4), 451-61.
5.  Sterling, J.W. (1964), 'A comparative examination of two modes of intoxication - an exploratory study of glue sniffing', Journal of Criminal Law, Criminology and Police Sciences, 55 (1), 94-9.
6.  Ackerly W.C. and Gibson, G. (1964), 'Lighter fluid "sniffing"', American Journal of Psychiatry, 120, 1056-61.
7.  Sokol, J. and Robinson, J.L. (1963), 'Glue sniffing', Western Medicine, 4, 192.
8.  Wyse, D.G. (1973), 'Deliberate inhalation of volatile hydrocarbons: a review', Canadian Medical Association Journal, 108, 71-4.
9.  Malcolm, A.I. (1968), 'Solvent sniffing and its effects', Addictions, 15, 12-21.
10. Stybel, L.J., Allen, P. and Lewis, F. (1976), 'Deliberate hydrocarbon inhalation among low socio-economic adolescents not necessarily apprehended by the police', International Journal of the Addictions, 11(2), 345-61.
11. Gregg, M. (1971), 'A note on solvent sniffing in Toronto', Addictions, 18, 39-44.
12. Ellison, W.S. (1965), 'Portrait of a glue sniffer', Crime and Delinquency, 11, 394-9.
13. Schottstaedt, M.F. and Bjork, J.W. (1977), 'Inhalant abuse in an Indian boarding school', American Journal of Psychiatry, 134(11), 1290-3.
14. Chapel, J.L. and Taylor, D.W. (1970), 'Drugs for Kicks', Crime and Delinquency, 16(1), 1-35.
15. Barker, G.H. and Adams, W.T. (1963), 'Glue sniffers', Sociology and Social Research, 47, 298-311.
16. Kupperstein, L.R. and Susman, R.M. (1968), 'A bibliography on the inhalation of glue fumes and other toxic vapours', International Journal of the Addictions, 3(1), 177-97.

17. Gellman, V. (1968), 'Glue sniffing among Canadian school children', Canadian Medical Association Journal, 98, 411-13.

18. Rubin, S.T. and Babb, J. (1968), The Glue Sniffer, Denver Juvenile Court.

19. Davis, R.F. (1967), 'The New York City Experience', Juvenile Court Judges Journal, 18, 53-5.

20. Kramer, J.P. (1972), 'The adolescent addict', Clinical Paediatrics, 11(7), 382-5.

21. D'Amanda, C., Plumb, M.M. and Taintor, Z. (1977), 'Heroin addicts with a history of glue sniffing: a deviant group within a deviant group', International Journal of the Addictions, 12(2-3), 255-70.

22. Watson, J.M. (1979), 'Solvent abuse: a retrospective study', Community medicine, 1(2), 153-6.

23. Ramsay, A. (1983), Solvent sniffing, Strathclyde Regional Council, Education Division.

24. Masterton, G. and Sclare, A.B. (1978), 'Solvent abuse', Health Bulletin, 36(6), 305-9.

25. Watson, J.M., Baird, J. and Sourindhrin, I. (1980) 'Solvent abuse, the East End Project', Strathclyde Police Guardian, 4(1), 21-6.

26. Sourindhrin, I. and Baird, J.A. (1984), 'Management of solvent misuse: a Glasgow community approach', British Journal of Addiction, 79, 227-32.

27. Campbell, D. and Watson, J.M. (1978), 'A comparative study of 18 glue sniffers', Community Health, 9(4), 207-10.

Chapter Five

SOLVENT ABUSE IN THE COMMUNITY

Review of the World Literature

The fact that the glue sniffing problem spread
geographically and grew numerically from the time
that the first incidents were reported has already
been described. It has been claimed that the
practice constituted a considerable community
threat in many parts of America and that it reached
epidemic proportions in some places. Reports about
the growing size and extent of the practice
appeared in both the medical journals and the
national press. It would seem from all these
reports that solvent abuse had indeed become a
dreadful problem. In spite of all this publicity,
it remains difficult to obtain incidence and
prevalence statistics on what was supposed to be a
common and widespread problem in some areas.
    An attempt was made in December 1962 to
measure the extent of the practice by the Hobby
Industry Association of America by conducting a
postal poll of 337 police chiefs in cities with
populations in excess of 50,000 in all states of
the USA. The poll was intended to measure the
extent to which glue sniffing was considered to be
a serious problem. Only 40 per cent of the police
chiefs responded and of those who did, 67 per cent
said that they had no problem, 18 per cent said
that they had a problem but that it was not serious
and 15 per cent said that they had a problem and it
was serious. Two points should be noted. No
information was obtained for 60 per cent of the
cities due to the failure of the police chiefs to
respond. Secondly, even for the cities which did
respond, each had its own set of criteria for
assessing juvenile offences so that the figures
obtained were not standardised and therefore it was

difficult to make accurate comparisons between cities.'

By the early 1960s, sufficient concern about the apparent size of the problem had been aroused among community and education groups, health departments, police departments and the press to lead to the introduction of legislation concerning solvent abuse in many of the states of the USA. This legislation was of two kinds. First, there was the approach which made it an offence to abuse volatile substances for their intoxicating properties, and secondly, there were laws which restricted the sale of intoxicating substances to minors.

The introduction of legislation made it possible to collect statistics about the extent of the problem. In Los Angeles, the number of arrests for glue sniffing rose from 41 to 136 between 1961 and 1962[2] and in Denver the number rose from 30 in 1960 to 184 in 1964.[3] In Chicago, 47 glue sniffers came to the attention of the police department in the six months between May and October 1962[4] and in New York, 2003 cases of glue sniffing were reported in 1963.[5] More recently, the Sheriff's Department in Los Angeles County arrested 180 juveniles under the age of 18 between July 1970 and July 1971 and in the same period the East Los Angeles Station arrested 79 juveniles.[6] While this information is better than none at all, it is still impossible to extract from such data the extent of the practice among those who were not seen by the police. Also, not all states introduced legislation that made glue sniffing illegal so that there are no statistics of this kind for them.

The clinical recording of interesting cases seen by doctors sometimes provided information on solvent abuse. For example, the chief physician at the Los Angeles County Probation Department investigated over 717 cases of glue sniffing in the period up to 1 April 1965. The Hawaii State Medical Association conducted a survey in 1971 among doctors asking them about drug abuse among the young people who were currently consulting them about their health. Replies were received from 393 and 17 per cent of these reported that they had seen solvent abuse during the previous 60 days. However, statistics from medical sources are also likely to be incomplete, one reason for this being the fact that working class and minority group people in America are less likely than others to seek medical help for adverse reactions to solvent abuse.

More accurate information has come from
surveys of drug abuse conducted in America, Canada
and Denmark. In a survey conducted by means of a
questionnaire circulated among 551 white, middle-class,
Jewish adolescents attending private schools in New
York, it was found that cleaning fluid or glue
fumes had been abused by 3 per cent of them.[7] A
much larger survey was conducted in Dallas in 1969
by means of questionnaires that were given to
57,000 students at 43 different senior and junior
high schools. The questions asked covered
comprehensively every aspect of drug use including
cigarettes and alcohol.[8] Different categories were
used to cover the various possible forms of solvent
abuse. It was found that 29 per cent of all the
young people had inhaled solvents at least once and
that solvents from glues were the most popular (10
per cent) followed by solvents in nail polish
remover (8 per cent) lighter fluid (5 per cent) and
aerosols sprays (3 per cent). During 1971, a survey
on previous drug abuse among 20,000 consecutive
male entrants to a military training centre in the
American Midwest revealed that 4 per cent admitted
to previous involvement in glue sniffing.[9] In
Denmark in 1972, an investigation by questionnaire
into the extent of drug abuse in two areas showed
that the prevalence of glue sniffing was 0.8 per
cent in one area and 0.9 per cent in the other.[10]

These surveys gave more information about the
extent of solvent abuse than had previously been
available but still had limitations. For example,
some of them requested information about glue
sniffing alone and did not include other forms of
solvent abuse. Another limitation in some was that
young people absent from school or college would
not be included and there is evidence that young
people who are involved in some kind of drug abuse
are likely to be absent more frequently. It is
possible that the surveys conducted in schools
might have underestimated the extent of all kinds
of drug abuse including solvent abuse. Again, some
of the surveys measured the extent of solvent abuse
at a specific point in time and therefore gave no
information about the rates of growth or decrease
of solvent abuse. Once again, vital information is
found to be missing.

A study of drug abuse among 6,500 schoolchildren
was carried out in Toronto between 1968 and 1970
and repeated in 1972 and 1974 in order to
investigate trends. The measured rate of glue

sniffing was 5.7 per cent in 1968, fell to 3.8 per cent in 1970, again fell to 2.9 per cent in 1972 but rose to 3.8 per cent in 1974.[11,12] The fluctuations are obvious but no explanations were given to account for them. A similar survey in Halifax, Nova Scotia, was carried out by means of a questionnaire completed by 1600 pupils in 1969 and 1970. It was found that the use of most drugs had increased and that the numbers sniffing glue had grown from 3.1 per cent in 1969 to 7.2 per cent in 1970.

In the USA since 1972, surveys have been conducted using household interviews.[13] The wording of the surveys has varied with respect to the questions about inhalant misuse. In 1972, the survey asked about 'glue or other things you breathe in' but by 1976 this had become 'glue or some other substances that people inhale for kicks or to get high. Besides glue there are other things like gasoline, some aerosols, nitrous oxide, amyl nitrite which is also called "poppers" and other solvents'. Small percentage differences were found to occur from year to year. For young people aged from 12 to 17, the extent of involvement in 1972 was 6.4 per cent rising to 8.1 per cent in 1975/76. The 1977 survey showed that 9 per cent of young people in the same age group had used glue at one time or another and that 0.7 per cent had done so within the previous month.[14] The 1979 figures were identical.[15] It is doubtful whether the small difference noted between 1972 and 1979 represents a real change in the national pattern of solvent abuse since the difference might simply have been caused by a random effect in the sampling. It is also emphasised that, while the figures are consistent in themselves, they may not have picked up trends at a community or group level.

Although there are considerable variations in the geographical extent of solvent abuse, it is clear that a large number of children and adolescents have experimented with the practice and it is obvious that it is the younger age groups in the population that have been most attracted to it. The authors of the 1979 national survey in the USA estimated that between 6.5 and 8.5 million people aged between 12 and 25 had experimented with solvent abuse but that half of them had only done so once or twice.[15] Although the numbers involved seem very large, the total exposure was minimal in half of the cases.

## The Extent of Solvent Abuse in Strathclyde

The remainder of this chapter discusses the extent of solvent abuse in Strathclyde. The problems of getting an accurate estimate of it are similar to those experienced in the rest of the world as described above.

Since many of the initial reports of individuals being involved in solvent abuse were obtained via the system of juvenile justice, it is important that the reader is familiar with the system that operates in Strathclyde, and indeed in Scotland as a whole, since it differs in some respects from that operating in England and Wales. The reader is referred to Appendix A for the necessary information.

## Police Statistics

As described earlier in this book, the first survey of solvent abuse in Strathclyde was based entirely on Lanarkshire police statistics since these represented the only data then available on the practice. Access to individual identifying details was not permitted.

Analysis of the 69 cases which had come to the attention of police personnel confirmed that the individuals who abused solvents were likely to be younger than those involved in drug abuse. It indicated that solvent abuse was largely a group activity involving mainly males aged between 9 and 17 years who had anti-social tendencies. There tended to be clusters of cases within certain schools and within certain geographical areas, not all of them deprived.[16]

Although the police statistics did give some information about solvent abuse in Lanarkshire, it was at once obvious that the figures regarding the practice were likely to be both incomplete and biased. For instance, they would not be likely to include those who had remained law abiding and who therefore had not attracted the attention of the police by being disorderly or committing a breach of the peace. Again the figures for the ratio of males to females could be biased because, in general, a higher proportion of males are apprehended than females. Also, it was possible that some local sections of the Community Involvement Branch could be more hard pressed by other demands on their time. As a result, the apparent rate of solvent abuse in those areas would be lower than elsewhere, not because the actual rate was lower but because the detection rate was lower. It is worthy of note that 66 of the 69 solvent abusers who had come to the attention of the police were still at school and, of these, 17 were notified by the police to the School Health Service on account of solvent abuse and another 25 to the Social Work Department.

## Lanarkshire School Survey

Although information collected about solvent abuse by agencies such as the police and others is useful, it is not usually the result of investigating solvent abuse itself but comes from an interest in some related activity. For example, the police were involved with solvent abuse because of the associated anti-social behaviour and because of their duty to care for juveniles who might be at risk. It is not, however, a remit of the police to carry out a survey of solvent abuse itself so that any statistics about the practice from them are essentially by-products of some other activity and tend to be fragmentary. The same is true for statistics from most other public agencies.

It became obvious to the author that the only satisfactory way to obtain a true estimate of the extent of solvent abuse in Lanarkshire was by contact with the children themselves. Thus a prevalence survey, to measure the extent of solvent abuse, was proposed with the following aims.

1.  To discover the extent of solvent abuse among the boys and girls in Lanarkshire schools.
2.  To discover the factors that influence pupils to start and to continue sniffing.
3.  To discover the age of the pupils involved.
4.  To discover what proportion had stopped sniffing and why.
5.  To discover whether initiation had been by a group or by an individual.
6.  To discover whether solvent abuse was a group or an individual activity.
7.  To discover whether any siblings had also sniffed solvents.
8.  To discover how the solvents were acquired.

> 9. To discover if the pupils were aware of the health hazards of solvent abuse.

The appropriate population for this survey was taken to be the pupils in the secondary classes of the Lanarkshire schools. Information about these was provided by the Director of Education for Lanarkshire after he had been contacted by the Principal School Medical Officer for Lanarkshire. At that time, the Director of Education administered 45 secondary and comprehensive schools with a total roll of 51,740 pupils aged between approximately 11 and 18 years.

Using a random sample of pupils throughout all the schools would have been the ideal for this survey but it was obviously impractical owing to the lack of time, money and the special staff needed to help administer the survey. It was therefore necessary to limit the scope of the survey to pupils in a small number of carefully selected schools. Since an average age of 13 had been found in the police sample, it was logical to narrow the field of the sample to children aged between 12 and 15 years and this corresponded roughly to the first three years of secondary education.

Eight schools were chosen for the sample with the deliberate intention of having a wide and representative range of educational establishments including urban and rural schools, Roman Catholic and non-denominational, old established and new comprehensive schools. The total roll of these eight schools was 11,939 of which 7,900 were pupils in the first three years. A further basis for selection was to ensure that schools in particular areas known to have a problem with solvent abuse could be included along with schools not known to have a problem. This allowed comparisons to be made and left scope for differentiating factors to emerge. Six of the schools, all in urban areas, had rolls of between 1,000 and 1,300 pupils while the remaining two, both rural, were much smaller.

In November 1973, permission to undertake the survey was requested and granted, Thereafter, the Assistant Director of Education wrote to the head teachers of the schools involved to explain the reasons for the survey and to invite their co-operation. This was followed by personal letters from the author to each head teacher which expanded on the information already given and which promised, in each case, complete medical confidentiality. A questionnaire was prepared in which questions were asked to determine age, sex and experience of cigarettes, alcohol and solvents. It was intended that it should be presented by the investigator or by a person or persons quite unconnected with the school staff in order to achieve complete neutrality of administration. No names were required so that the children could be assured of complete anonymity.

Preparation of the questionnaire was nearing completion when, on Wednesday 23 January 1973, the Scottish Daily Express gave front page coverage to the proposed survey in the fullest detail. This was followed, on the evening of the same day, by an article in the Evening Times, a Glasgow newspaper, and the Daily Express for the next day published an editorial article on the subject. This produced indignant reactions from various sectors of the community. The questionnaire was rendered useless and the prevalence study of solvent abuse in Lanarkshire had to be abandoned.

Several factors relating to the proposed survey are obvious. If it had escaped publicity during the early stages, it would still have been vulnerable later, perhaps at the time when the questionnaires were being issued. Since the prevalence of solvent abuse was thought at that time to be low, it would have been necessary to question a large sample of children in order to ensure accurate results and this would have raised difficulties of management. Another possible limitation of a school survey has already been noted and is due to the link between solvent abuse and truancy which was suggested by the Lanarkshire police and supported by some American authors. If this is the case, then any prevalence study carried out in the schools would not reach some of those to whom it was directed and would thereby mask the true position. Any of these factors would have made it difficult to interpret the results accurately and by this stage the reader should be beginning to appreciate the difficulties in obtaining true figures for the extent of solvent abuse among our young people.

## Community Survey of Solvent Abuse

In order to obtain further information about the extent and trends of solvent abuse in Lanarkshire, evidence was compiled by studying the statistics from the police, from social work departments, from Lanarkshire's assessment centre and from hospital referrals. Each of these sources provided a proportion of the information for an analysis of the known, if not total, extent of the practice during the period between 1970 and 1975. This information was acquired retrospectively from the different sources and subsequently collated.

Altogether, 526 young people were found to have been involved in solvent abuse between 1970 and 1975, 87 per cent of these being male and 13 per cent female. The ages ranged from 6 to 19 for the males and from 9 to 18 for the females.

Most of the cases were found to have come to the attention of the police, the main reasons for attracting attention being:

1. Breach of the peace while under the influence of solvents.
2. Behaving in an apparently drunk and disorderly fashion.
3. Reported as missing from home.

However, as time went on, other children were brought to the attention of the police by parents or neighbours specifically because of known solvent abuse. In total, information about 72 per cent of the 526 young people known to have been involved came from police sources. Some of these cases were notified to the School Health Service or to the Social Work Department by the police while others were thought not to require any such referral.

A further 14 per cent of these 526 cases came to the attention of social workers. As solvent abuse was not at that time considered a specific ground for referral under the Social Work (Scotland) Act 1968, it was not included in the official social work returns. However, at local social work offices, social workers had sometimes recorded solvent abuse along with other details about the children with whom they were involved. Clearly, the recording of this information depended on a number of factors such as the work load of the individual social workers and whether they personally regarded solvent abuse as a form of problem behaviour. Because of this, it was not possible to state the extent to which solvent abuse featured in the social work cases as a whole but the number involved was not thought to be significantly large. Of the 88 individuals known to the social work agencies, 14 were also known to the police and were excluded. The remainder contributed 14 per cent of the total cases of solvent abuse described above.

A study of the case records of the Lanarkshire assessment centre provided additional useful information. Excluding the period from January to July 1975, only 1.7 per cent of the 1,042 case records of admissions to the assessment centre contained any reference to solvent abuse. Since the subjects, mainly male, had been admitted as being in need of care and protection or because of deviant behaviour of one kind or another unconnected with sniffing practices, it would seem that solvent abuse represented only a small facet of deviance. However, as in the case of the social work records, the noting of solvent abuse in any individual case would depend to some extent on the attitude to solvent abuse of the staff members concerned. Of the 18 teenagers found to be involved in solvent abuse, 4 were already known to the police and were not included for a second time. However, of the 121 Lanarkshire children admitted consecutively to the assessment centre between 1 January and 31 March 1975, 25 (21 per cent) had been involved in solvent abuse. The total of 39 cases of solvent abusers from the assessment centre represented 8 per cent of the 526 known solvent abusers between 1970 and 1975. An additional 2 per cent were referred to the author by their parents specifically because of solvent abuse. They were not known to the police, to social workers or to the assessment centre.

None of the individuals mentioned had attended hospital on account of solvent abuse but a study of the records for in-patients and out-patients for 1970 to 1975 showed that 17 Lanarkshire children had arrived at hospitals in Lanarkshire in a state of intoxication following episodes of solvent abuse. Of these, eight had been examined and sent home and the remaining nine were admitted to the wards. Seven were kept in hospital for an overnight stay only and the other two remained for three or four days. Two young people in Lanarkshire died between 1970 and 1975 in incidents involving solvent abuse. One was not known to any of the agencies but the other was known by the police to have been involved in solvent abuse from time to time. The individuals who had been seen at hospitals or who had died contributed 4 per cent of the total.

In this study, it was possible to ensure that individuals were not included more than once in the statistical information since the author was

97

permitted access to the records on a confidential basis.

An analysis of the statistics from these 526 cases showed that, irrespective of the methods by which the children were referred, the average age was remarkably constant, between 13.5 and 15.5 years for males and 14 and 15.5 for females. This was true for each consecutive year of the study. It was not possible to make an accurate estimate of the total extent of solvent abuse in Lanarkshire for this period since there was no way of ascertaining how many cases had remained undetected. It is possible that this number was small but the fact that those individuals who became ill enough to be taken to hospital while glue sniffing had not been discovered by any of the other agencies suggests that the number missed might be large.

Trends in Solvent Abuse in Lanarkshire

It was obvious once all the information from the various sources was collated that, between 1 January 1970 and 31 December 1975, solvent abuse had increased among children and adolescents in Lanarkshire (Figure 5.1). Altogether, 12 young persons were involved in 1970, 53 in 1971, 27 in 1972, 113 in 1973, 90 in 1974 and 231 in 1975.

Figure 5.1: Total Number of Sniffers in Lanarkshire 1970-1975

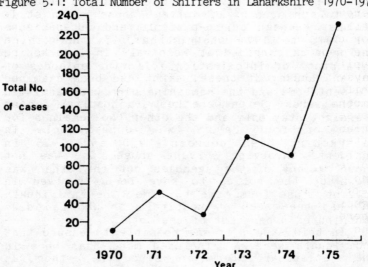

Solvent Abuse in the Community

The place of residence for each individual was noted for each year of involvement in an attempt to determine the extent of the practice in each district of Lanarkshire during the period of the study. The total male and female populations in each appropriate age band for each district were calculated from the 1971 census data. Involvement in solvent abuse in the different districts varied from 0.3 to 22.5 per thousand for males and from 0.4 to 8.1 per thousand for females. Although more common in some areas than others, known solvent abuse involved only small sectors of the population in any area. It was obvious by 1973 that the practice had become more widespread among both males and females and it was clear, despite the occasional decrease, that there was a trend towards an increasing degree of involvement of males in every area. Conversely, in the case of females, involvement in the practice showed a steady decline in every area except one. The known overall extent of solvent abuse was of the order of 1 per cent of the adolescent population for any year of the study.

Unfortunately, information about the schools attended was not always available, mainly because it was not included in the hospital and social work records but also because it was sometimes omitted from the police contact cards. The information available showed that there was considerable variation in the extent of solvent abuse in different schools and these differences were noted for schools within the same district as well as between schools in different districts. For example, in one district in 1975, the rate in the schools ranged from 9.9 to 33.7 per thousand pupils. This information, while inaccurate in many ways, seemed to confirm that obtained from the children themselves which was that the single most important factor in starting and stopping solvent abuse was the influence of friends at school or friends living locally who were also likely to attend the same school.[17]

These figures gave some idea of the extent of solvent abuse between 1970 and 1975 in Lanarkshire and indicated that cases known to the agencies represented a very small proportion of young people in any year. However, it was obvious that there were others who had also been involved and who had not come to the attention of the police, social workers or parents nor had they been admitted to hospitals or assessment centres. Indeed,

99

those known to be involved had indicated that many
more children were indulging in the practice than
were being detected and that many more incidents
occurred than were noted. The number of these
undetected sniffers was unknown as was the extent
of their involvement. Also, the rate of detection
and the recording of cases of solvent abuse
depended on the knowledge and attitudes of the
professional people who might have contact with it.
It is not clear to what extent this influenced the
statistics relating to involvement in the practice.

Glasgow
By 1975, as well as the two deaths in Lanarkshire
already described, there were four deaths among
adolescents in Glasgow which could be attributed to
some aspect of solvent abuse. By June 1976,
sufficient concern had been engendered about
solvent abuse among the young people in the East
End of Glasgow to lead to the formation of a
solvent abuse group for the area comprising all
interested professional parties. The intention of
this group was to study and evaluate the problem
and to facilitate the free exchange of information
about individual problems which arose.
     In August 1976, a schoolboy from a secondary
school in the East End died and, as a result, it
was decided to assess the extent of solvent abuse
in that particular school. Therefore, in October of
that year, the 898 pupils of the school, aged from
11 to 16, were assembled under examination
conditions and each was given a questionnaire and a
pencil. The pupils were told to put their ages on
the paper but not names and were forbidden to show
the questionnaire to anyone else while completing
it. The questions asked were simple and unambiguous
and were designed to determine the extent and
frequency of solvent abuse, the method of acquiring
the substances used and knowledge of the dangers
involved.[18]
     The overall extent of those who had tried
solvent abuse was found to be 9.8 per cent but it
should be noted that this included both those who
had tried and stopped and those who were still
active. The highest involvement rates were among
pupils aged between 13 and 15 (Table 5.1). Of those
who had been involved, 50 per cent had done so only
once, a further 28 per cent had tried it more than
once but not regularly, and 22 per cent had been
involved regularly. However, there was no way of

Solvent Abuse in the Community

assessing what 'regularly' meant. It was concluded that half of the sniffers had been introduced to the practice by friends. Of those who indulged, 9 per cent said that they were unaware of the dangers as compared with 14 per cent of those who had not indulged.

Table 5.1: Surveys of Extent of Solvent Abuse in a Glasgow School 1976-1982*

| Age | 1976 | 1979 | 1982 |
|-----|------|------|------|
| 11 | 6.7 | 5.5 | 3.1 |
| 12 | 6.0 | 9.8 | 12.7 |
| 13 | 9.1 | 17.7 | 24.3 |
| 14 | 16.1 | 18.3 | 21.9 |
| 15 | 11.4 | 17.2 | 23.7 |
| 16 | nil | nil | nil |
| All ages | 9.8 | 14.1 | 18.9 |

* This table gives the percentage of each age group who admitted to involvement in solvent abuse.

The survey was repeated in October 1979 when the extent of involvement was found to be 14 per cent, the highest rates again occurring among those aged between 13 and 15 years. This time 35 per cent had tried once only, 33 per cent had tried more than once, but not regularly, and 32 per cent reported regular use. (Figure 5.2). Repeating this in October 1982 gave a rate of involvement of 19 per cent with the same age band for the highest involvement. Almost half (47 per cent) had indulged only once, 32 per cent had been involved more than once but not on a regular basis, and 21 per cent had been involved regularly. About half of the sniffers who had been involved to any extent had been introduced to the activity by friends.

Figure 5.2: Glasgow School Survey: Involvement in Solvent Abuse 1976-1982

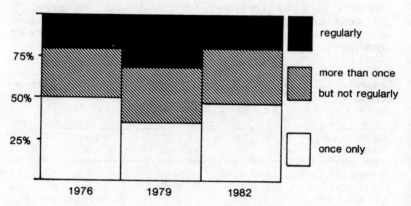

All these surveys were carried out under identical circumstances so that there was compatibility between them and a number of conclusions can be drawn. Firstly, the ages of highest risk were 13-15 years. It could also be concluded that the number of pupils abusing solvents had increased steadily between October 1976 and October 1982. There was a noticeable increase in the fraction of abusers involved regularly in 1979 followed by a decrease in 1982 but, when expressed as a fraction of the total school population, the number of regular abusers was found to have increased from about 2 per cent to 4 per cent between 1976 and 1979 and then to have stayed at about this level in 1982.

These studies of the trends in a single school in the East End of Glasgow are the only attempt at a prevalence study within a school population in Strathclyde. It undoubtedly shows an increase between 1976 and 1982 but it is not possible from this study alone to apply the results to the juvenile population as a whole.

## The East End Project

Under the auspices of a grant from the British Medical Association, a study of solvent abuse in the east end of Glasgow was set up by the author with the approval of the Greater Glasgow Health Board and the Strathclyde Police. It was intended to run for one year as a screening clinic for individuals who had been involved in solvent abuse. It was planned to offer a medical examination,

which would include the taking of a blood sample as
a check for abnormalities, to all those who wanted
this done. At the same time, it would be possible
to collect information about the practice and its
participants in the area. The clinic was held in
the medical room of the Tobago Street Police
Station because this facility was offered by the
police who were concerned about the problem and
because no other suitable premises were available.
During the year of the study, 196 young persons
were referred and 134 actually attended.

The postal code for the place of residence of
each of the 134 cases was used to determine the
extent of solvent abuse in different districts of
the East End. The population aged from 5 to 15
years in each appropriate district at mid-year in
1978 was used as the baseline population. Although
it was realised that these statistics gave only a
rough approximation, it was hoped that, in the
absence of more accurate data, they might still
give a guide to the extent of the practice.[19] The
rate of involvement thus obtained varied from 0.9
to 11.1 per thousand and indicated that, although
more common in some districts than others, solvent
abuse everywhere affected only a small sector of
the youthful population. However, any sample based
on attendance at a clinic in a police station is
likely to be biased and it is possible that a
significant number of abusers may have been missed.

## Strathclyde Police Statistics

The police have collected statistical information
on solvent abuse throughout Strathclyde since 1977
by means of the contact card system for juveniles
(This is described in Appendix A). The numbers thus
obtained are restricted to juveniles under the age
of 16 for whom the police have a responsibility of
care and protection. The number of cases of solvent
abuse, shown in Table 5.2, has risen from 530 to a
peak of 1,725 in 1981 but has since fallen
significantly to 1,111. They are the only
statistics on the extent of solvent abuse to have
been collected consistently over the last few years
and are accurate as far as they go. Their
limitation is that they only give information about
solvent abusers who come to the attention of the
police because of problem behaviour of one kind or
another. Most, but not all, of the cases occurred
within the Greater Glasgow area and the age range
was approximately 10 to 16 years. The estimated

population of those aged from 10 to 16 in the area covered by the Greater Glasgow Health Board on 30 June 1981 was 119,713 which, taken in conjunction with the 1,725 cases of solvent abusers known to the police, gives an estimate of 1.2 per cent of the juvenile population as having come to the attention of the police on account of solvent abuse. The variation from year to year is large. The police statistics do not contain any information about the substances abused and there is, of course, no information about the extent of solvent abuse which did not come to the attention of the police.

Table 5.2: Number of Strathclyde Police Cases of Solvent Abuse 1977-1983

|          | 1977 | 1978 | 1979 | 1980 | 1981 | 1982 | 1983 |
|----------|------|------|------|------|------|------|------|
| Males    |      | 1040 | 1219 | 1342 | 1485 | 991  | 920  |
| Females  |      | 113  | 244  | 218  | 240  | 148  | 191  |
| Total    | 530  | 1153 | 1463 | 1560 | 1725 | 1139 | 1111 |

## The List D School Survey

A survey of solvent abuse was carried out in a List D school in Strathclyde in 1981 by two field workers from community field volunteers.[20] It was carried out using a low-key formal approach in which the boys were engaged in natural conversation in informal circumstances. Interviews were carried out with 62 boys aged from 12 to 16. Typically, they came from areas of urban deprivation and from homes in which the average family size was four to five children. Two-thirds of their parents were unemployed and most of the boys had been involved in truancy at one time or another.

Of these 62 boys, 29 had never abused solvents and one-third of the remaining 33 were ex-sniffers. Two-thirds of the active sniffers were said to be habitual sniffers and the peak ages for involvement were 14 and 15 which presumably implied a lengthy sniffing history in some cases. Apart from solvent abuse, the characteristics of the abusers and non-abusers were similar. These results showed that

within the context of that particular List D
setting, 50 per cent of the children had abused
solvents and two-thirds of these were habitual
sniffers. In all cases the solvent abuse had taken
the form of glue sniffing as such, although in a
few cases leather conditioner, spray paint and
petrol had also featured. The report was completed
in May 1981.

This survey was interesting and relevant but
because of its narrow terms of reference it did not
give information about some aspects of wider
involvement in solvent abuse. However, a more
extensive survey was carried out by Strathclyde
Social Work Department in May 1982

Strathclyde Social Work Survey
This survey was carried out by questionnaire and
the results became available in April 1983. The
establishments involved were

    1. Children's homes belonging to local
       authority and voluntary organisations.
    2. Residential assessment centres.
    3. Intermediate training centres.
    4. List D schools.

In all, 134 questionnaires were circulated with the
intention of finding out the numbers of children in
these establishments who had been involved in
solvent abuse. It was also hoped that it would
provide information on the different proportions of
solvent abuse in these different types of
establishment and about solvent abuse in general,
including any associated problems. Questionnaires
were returned from 108 establishments giving a
total response rate of 81 per cent. This rate was
higher for the childrens' homes and assessment
centres (93 per cent) than for the intermediate
training centres and List D schools (48 per cent).

A total of 254 abusers were identified from a
total of 2,396 children (11 per cent). The numbers
and variation between the different types of
establishment is given in Table 5.3. Despite the
lower response rate from the List D schools, it is
clear from those who replied that they had the
highest percentage of abusers (33 per cent)
which is in marked contrast to the rate in the
children's homes (4 per cent). Based on a subset of
163 children from the 254 abusers, three types of
solvent abusers were identified as experimental,

Table 5.3: Strathclyde Survey of Solvent Abusers in Social Work Establishments, May 1982

| | Number of establishments surveyed | Number of responses | Number of establishments with solvent abuse | Number of abusers |
|---|---|---|---|---|
| Local authority children's homes | 67 | 64 | 18 | 43 |
| Voluntary children's homes | 18 | 17 | 3 | 13 |
| Assessment centres | 7 | 7 | 4 | 10 |
| Intermediate training centres | 18 | 8 | 5 | 72 |
| List D schools | 24 | 12 | 9 | 116 |
| Totals | 134 | 108 | 39 | 254 |

regular and chronic although a precise definition of these terms was not given and it is possible that they were interpreted differently by different establishments. As is shown in Table 5.4, the proportions of the different types of involvement varied with the type of establishment.[21]

Table 5.4: Types of Solvent Abuse identified in Strathclyde Social Work Establishments, May 1982

|  | Experimental (%) | Regular (%) | Chronic (%) |
| --- | --- | --- | --- |
| Local authority children's homes | 59 | 36 | 5 |
| Voluntary children's homes | 58 | 33 | 8 |
| Assessment centres | 30 | 50 | 20 |
| Intermediate training centres | 42 | 24 | 34 |
| List D schools | 11 | 56 | 33 |

Although the results showed that overall four out of every five abusers were male, there were marked differences between establishments with the percentage of abusers being male varying from 77 per cent in the childrens' homes to 17 per cent in the voluntary homes. This variation may have been due to different total numbers of boys and girls in these places but this was not made clear since no information was given about the male to female ratios in the base populations. In the assessment centres, there were found to be three male to two female abusers. The age range was given as 10 to 18 years with 55 per cent falling into the 14 to 15 years range. The duration of involvement varied from less than five months to more than five years and a large majority of the children (80 per cent) had been involved in solvent abuse for more than one year.

Solvent Abuse in the Community

Statistics from the Information and Resource Unit
on Addiction
This unit opened in Glasgow in 1982 and between 2
August 1982 and 30 September 1983, dealt with 2,125
enquiries received by telephone, letters or
personal calls, 37 per cent of which were about
solvents. The various categories are shown in Table
5.5. Although the percentage of calls about
solvents has been high, it fell to 28 per cent
between October 1983 and September 1984. The
information officer has analysed the calls and
discovered that most had come from professionals or
other interested people who were seeking information
and less than 10 per cent had come from individuals
with problems involving solvent abuse. The largest
number of 'problem' calls were apparently about
drugs, mainly heroin, cannabis and minor tranquillisers.[22]

Table 5.5: Enquiries to the Glasgow Information and Resource
Unit on Addiction 1982-1984

|  | Aug. 1982 - Sept.1983 | Oct. 1983 - Sept. 1984 |
|---|---|---|
| Alcohol | 487 (23%) | 228 (18%) |
| Drugs | 789 (37%) | 647 (51%) |
| Solvents | 794 (37%) | 350 (28%) |
| Gambling | 55 ( 3%) | 23 ( 3%) |
| Totals | 2125 | 1248 |

This information is interesting because it
indicates the relative public concern about solvent
abuse in relation to other problems of abuse but it
does not add anything useful to the statistical
data about the numbers of people abusing solvents.

Referrals to the Reporter
It was only in July 1983 that solvent abuse became
a specific ground for referral to the Reporter to
the Children's Panel under the Social Work
(Scotland) Act (1968). The consequences of this
have already appeared in the returns made to the
Social Work Services Group by reporters and their
departments.
    In Strathclyde, between July 1983 and July
1984, 461 referrals were made to the Reporter on

account of solvent abuse. The ages of the children
involved ranged from 7 to 17 years, the majority
being aged between 13 and 15. These 461 referrals
may, and probably do, represent a smaller number of
individual children since some may have been
referred more than once and the statistics refer to
individual referrals and not to individual
children. The sources of referral (Table 5.6) were
the police, the Procurator Fiscal, education
departments, health sources, social work departments,
the RSSPCC and parents.[23]

It was relevant to note that 184 (40 per cent)
had no previous referrals to the Reporter's office.
The actions that were taken about these children
under the Social Work (Scotland) Act were that 50
per cent were referred to the Children's Panel and
the remainder were discharged. Half of those
referred to the Children's Panel were made the
subjects of a supervision order.[23]

Table 5.6: Referrals to the Strathclyde Reporter on Account
of Solvent Abuse 1983-1984

| Source of referral | Number of referrals | |
|---|---|---|
| Police | 424 | (92%) |
| Procurator Fiscal | 20 | (4.4%) |
| Social Work Dept. | 2 | (0.4%) |
| Parents | 2 | (0.4%) |
| Education Dept. | 11 | (2.4%) |
| Health authorities | 1 | (0.2%) |
| RSSPCC | 1 | (0.2%) |
| | 461 | |

Conclusions

It can be clearly stated, in summary, that the
extent of solvent abuse in Strathclyde has never
been accurately measured but the practice is
demonstrably not restricted to any one district or
any one group. It has been shown that the overall
figures for known abusers, incomplete as they
undoubtedly are for a variety of reasons, when
compared to the total number of abusers, indicate
that solvent abuse affects only a small proportion

of the juveniles in any area and that the practice comes and goes from time to time and place to place. There is no evidence to substantiate the claims that it has ever been a numerically large problem over the years when considered in terms of the total population. Indeed, the evidence that is available from what was Lanarkshire, now the Lanark division of Strathclyde, and from Glasgow suggests an overall rate of about one per cent. The possible inaccuracies of this figure have already been described.

The extent of involvement in solvent abuse has been found to vary with time among certain groups of school children attending a particular school in Glasgow with the rate increasing from 10 to 18 per cent over a number of years. It should be noted that most of these young people were not active abusers at the time of the survey. However, a report in May 1981 indicated that 50 per cent of the boys in one List D school had been involved in solvent abuse, two-thirds of them being habitually involved. The more extensive 1982 survey of social work establishments found that 11 per cent of the children in these places were involved but the rates in different types of establishments varied from 4 to 33 per cent, the latter being the rate in the List D schools. Information about the degree and type of involvement was available for a subset of these children and showed that there were three kinds of involvement; 'experimental', 'regular' and 'chronic' although the use of these terms was not clearly defined and may not even have been applied in a consistent manner throughout the survey. The Strathclyde Police statistics, kept since 1977, indicate fluctuations in the known numbers of young people involved in solvent abuse although there is no further information about the details of the methods used or the extent of individual participation. The most recent figures show a great reduction in the overall numbers. The Reporter's figures, available since solvent abuse became a ground for referral in July 1983, show that many referrals have been made, mainly by the police, but these may have included multiple referrals of the same children. About 30 per cent of the children referred had not been previously referred to the Reporter.

Despite the fluctuations which have been noted it is obvious that solvent abuse has involved only a small fraction of the children and adolescents in Strathclyde. It also seems clear that at any given time only a proportion of those who have admitted to solvent abuse are currently active and that the remainder could be more properly called former solvent abusers since they were involved for only a few sessions and then stopped. This seems to contradict headlines such as 'Half Our Kids Sniff Glue' or 'Epidemic of Glue Sniffing' which have appeared in the media, and refutes the belief held by many members of the public that glue sniffing is common. It is also stated that the rate of solvent abuse is high but there are no figures from any study within the community of Strathclyde to support this. One of the reasons for believing that glue sniffing is a common practice may be that, although it is a clandestine activity, its associated problems such as occasional noisy behaviour, accidents and infrequent sudden deaths are dramatic and highly visible events which draw an undue amount of attention to the practice. In comparison, the many other young people going about their ordinary non-sniffing business are, comparatively speaking, invisible because they do not draw attention to themselves or their activities. Consequently, the public tends to be very aware of solvent abuse in Strathclyde but unable to see it in its proper perspective.

It is also clear from these results that the rates are higher in certain groups such as those in residential establishments although there are marked differences between establishments. The association between juvenile delinquency and solvent abuse has been noted first in America and subsequently in some of the Strathclyde studies. However, the exact nature of the association has not been determined. While it is clear that solvent abuse occurs more frequently among those whose behaviour has been labelled as deviant, it is not clear whether solvent abuse caused the delinquent behaviour or was caused by it. However, the fact that two-fifths of those referred to the Reporter for solvent abuse had not been previously involved in anti-social activities would tend to confirm that solvent abuse need not mean that an individual will show deviant behaviour.

REFERENCES

1. Press, E. and Done, A.K. (1967) 'Solvent sniffing', Paediatrics, 39(4) 451-61.
2. Barker, G.H. and Adams, W.T. (1963) 'Glue sniffers', Sociology and Social Research, 47, 298-311.
3. Corliss, L.M. (1965), 'A review of evidence on glue sniffing - a persistent problem', Journal of School Health, 35, 442-9.
4. Sterling, J.W. (1964), 'A comparative examination of two modes of intoxication - an exploratory study of glue sniffing', Journal of Criminal Law, Criminology and Police Sciences, 55(1), 94-9.
5. Allen, S.M. (1966), 'Glue sniffing', International Journal of the Addictions, 1, 147-9.
6. Sokol, J. (1973), 'A survey of the inhaling of solvent among teenagers', in Drugs and Youth, (ed.) E. Harms, Pergamon Press, pp. 73-90.
7. Milman, D.H. and Su, W. (1973), 'Patterns of illicit drugs and alcohol use among secondary students', Journal of Paediatrics, 83(2), 314-20.
8. Gossett, J.T., Lewis, J.M. and Phillips, V.A. (1971), 'Extent and prevalence of illicit drugs use as reported by 56,745 students', Journal of the American Medical Association, 216(9), 1464-70.
9. Patterson, C.D. (1974), 'Self-reported unpleasant effects from illicit use of fourteen substances', British Journal of Addiction, 69, 249-56.
10. Boolsen, M.W. (1975), 'Drugs in Denmark', International Journal of the Addictions, 10(3), 503-12.
11. Fejer, D. Smart, R.G. and Whitehead, P.C. (1972), 'Changes in the patterns of drug abuse in two Canadian cities: Toronto and Halifax', International Journal of the Addictions, 7(3), 467-79.
12. Smart, R.G. and Fejer, D. (1975), 'Six years of cross sectional surveys of student drug use in Toronto', Bulletin on Narcotics, 27(2), 11-22.
13. Sharp, C.W. and Brehm, M.L. (1977), Review of inhalants: Euphoria to dysfunction NIDA Research Monograph 15, 18-19, National Institute on Drug Abuse, USA.
14. Mason, T. (1979), Inhalant use and treatment, DHEW Publication No. (ADM) 79-783, US Department of Health, Education and Welfare.

Solvent Abuse in the Community

15. Fishburn, P.H., Abelson, H.I. and Cisin,
I. (1980), <u>National survey on drug abuse: main
findings: 1979</u>, DHSS Publication No. (ADM) 80-976,
US Department of Health and Human Services.
16. Watson, J.M. (1975), 'A study of solvent
sniffing in Lanarkshire', <u>Health Bulletin</u>, <u>23</u>(4)
153-5.
17. Watson, J.M. (1980), 'Trends in solvent
abuse', <u>Strathclyde Police Guardian</u>, <u>4</u>(2), 29-32.
18. Ramsay, A. (1982), <u>Solvent sniffing</u>,
Department of Education, Strathclyde Regional
Council.
19. Watson, J.M., Baird, J. and Sourindhrin,
I. (1980), 'Solvent abuse: the East End Project',
<u>Strathclyde Police Guardian</u>, <u>4</u>(1), 21-6.
20. Roberts, H. and Anderson, M. (1981),
<u>Kerelaw Project</u>, Social Work Department, Ayr
Division, Strathclyde Regional Council.
21. Isles, G. (1983), 'Survey of solvent abuse
in individual establishments', Social Work Department,
Strathclyde Regional Council, Glasgow.
22. Fraser, J. (1984), <u>Information and
Resource Unit on Addiction: statistics</u>. Social Work
Department, Strathclyde Regional Council, Glasgow.
23. Kennedy, F. (1985), 'Reporter's Office
statistics on solvent abuse', personal communication.
<u>Reporter's Office, Strathclyde Regional Council,
Glasgow</u>.

Chapter Six

THE MEDICAL EFFECTS

> The services rendered by intoxicating substances
> in the struggle for happiness and in warding
> off misery rank so highly as a benefit that
> both individuals and races have given them an
> established position within the libido-economy.
> It is not merely the immediate gain in
> pleasure which one owes to them, but also a
> measure of that independence of the outer
> world which is sorely craved .... We are aware
> that it is just this property which constitutes
> the danger and injuriousness of intoxicating
> substances ...

Freud, S. (1939)

Intoxication by Inhalation

During the process of breathing air enters the
lungs through the nose and mouth, passes down
through the throat and windpipe and enters the
lungs. There, the gases in the air dissolve in the
blood and are pumped by the heart around the body
to the various organs. These extract the oxygen
they require from the blood and give up carbon
dioxide as a waste product. This, in turn, is
dissolved in the blood and pumped to the lungs
where it is breathed out.

In the case of solvent abuse, vapours from the
various substances get into and out of the body in
exactly the same way as oxygen and carbon dioxide.
The abuse of volatile chemicals does not simply
involve 'sniffing' but requires deep inhalation
through the nose and mouth. The process as
described by the children consisted of taking
several deep breaths until the desired degree of

intoxication was achieved. There would be a pause and then the cycle would be repeated. Solvent vapours from glues and other products are readily absorbed into the body due to the large surface area of the lungs. This ensures a rapid onset of effect, almost as quick as that from the intravenous injection of a drug. The resulting action on the brain causes intoxication which is the effect desired by the sniffers.

In the brain, these substances become attached to fats which are plentiful there. The solvents leave the body by being breathed out again, by being chemically altered in the liver or by being filtered out through the kidneys. All this occurs as they are pumped around the body by the heart. Although there is a great deal of information about the effects of solvents, their mechanism of action on the body is not understood but it would be expected that the organs likely to be most affected are the brain, liver, kidneys and heart.

## Introduction
The world literature contains many reports of injury, accident, health damage and deaths associated with solvent abuse.[1,2,3,4] Despite these, a great deal of confusion still remains regarding the effects of solvent abuse, their incidence and their significance. These are discussed in this chapter and are presented in four sections - immediate effects, psychological effects, long-term physical effects and deaths.

## The Immediate Effects

The immediate or acute effects of solvent abuse can be defined as those seen during or just after a session. To obtain detailed information about these, the author interviewed, assessed and examined 335 young people immediately following sessions of solvent abuse in Lanarkshire and Glasgow between 1975 and 1984. The ages ranged from 8 to 19 years, most being between 13 and 15. They were seen in a variety of places; in their own homes, in police offices, in social work offices, in assessment centres, in doctors' surgeries and sometimes in actual glue sniffing dens such as lock-ups, caves or corners of wasteground. None was seen in hospital. Most (84 per cent) were seen within 30 to 90 minutes of the session and the rest were seen within three hours. The effects caused by the solvent abuse were noted and information was also collected from the young people about their medical histories and the effects of previous solvent abuse, including accidents, coma and episodes of hospitalisation. In most cases confirmatory evidence was obtained directly from parents or friends.

## Results of the Examinations

These young people turned out to be normal in all major respects when examined physically, showing no evidence of abnormalities of heart, lungs or abdomen which could be directly related to solvent abuse. Sometimes there were signs of glue on the face, hands, body or clothes (see Figures 6.1, 6.2 and 6.3) and in all cases there was a strong chemical smell from the breath which persisted for several hours after the episode.

Figure 6.1: Adhesive Stains on the Face

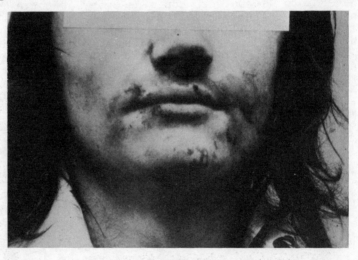

Source: Reproduced by kind permission of John Wright and Sons Ltd.

Figure 6.2: Adhesive Stains on the Neck

Source: Reproduced by kind permission of the editor, <u>The</u> <u>Practitioner</u>

Figure 6.3: Adhesive Marks on the Back

Source: Reproduced by kind permission of the editor, <u>The</u> <u>Practitioner</u>.

Regardless of the substance abused or the method employed, the early effects on the nervous system were found to be similar to those of acute alcoholic intoxication. Mild and fleeting excitement or pleasurable feelings were noted in many cases and it is possible that these in themselves may have been all that the sniffers sought by way of satisfaction. Occasionally, coughing, sneezing and nausea were found along with the excitement. This state of mild intoxication was apparently achieved within a few minutes and the return to normal also occurred quickly but was not so immediate as the onset of the effects. In the case of 80 per cent of the individuals there was no desire to go any further and at this early stage there are few potential hazards. However, in the remaining 20 per cent of cases, the solvent abuse continued well beyond this initial stage and thereafter depression of the nervous system occurred with subsequent loss of control over behaviour, confusion, loss of awareness of surroundings and loss of judgement followed by loss of control over muscles and co-ordination, drowsiness and finally coma (Figure 6.4). This range of effects,from euphoria to coma is very similar in pattern to that seen in acute alcoholic intoxication.

The duration and degree of intoxication depends not only on the dose of the substance but also on the degree of experience on the part of the sniffer. Habitual sniffers, for example, might require several tubes of glue or cans of aerosol in order to achieve a high level of intoxication but a novice would require much less before reaching the same level. The resultant period of intoxication might last anything from 15 minutes to a few hours but in 90 per cent of cases the length did not exceed one hour and only infrequently lasted for more than one and a half hours. There were four exceptional cases of individuals with very serious personal problems, who became very intoxicated and, although conscious, remained unresponsive for up to 48 hours. This was thought to be due to underlying emotional distress and all eventually recovered. 'Topping up' with solvent lengthens the duration of the effect and for habitual sniffers is the normal practice. This ensures that they never become excessively intoxicated, except by choice, and they can control the level of intoxication to achieve exactly the effect they wish. Inexperienced sniffers, on the other hand, did not always know what they were hoping to achieve by way of sensation and seemed to have much less control over the degree of intoxication which they induced.

Figure 6.4: The Acute Effects of Solvent Abuse

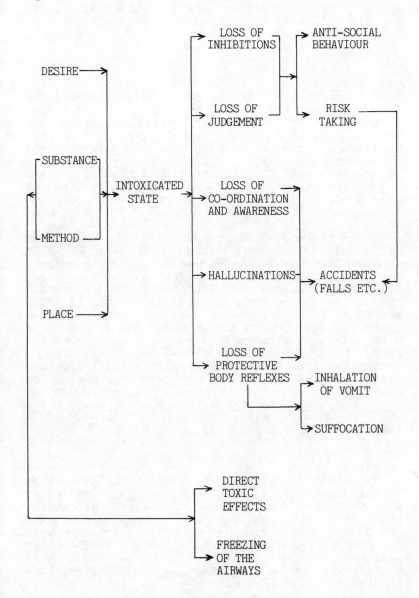

Some of the young people exhibited very aggressive behaviour while intoxicated while others became calm, happy and relaxed. It was thought that cultural and personality factors played a large part in determining this behaviour. In other words, the solvent intoxication merely released aggression but did not cause it. Again, this is similar to the situation in which aggression is released by alcohol in certain individuals.

## Hallucinations

The young people interpreted hallucinations as 'seeing things that are not there' or 'hearing things that are not there'. Vivid hallucinations were a feature described by 31 per cent of the individuals and were reported as being mainly visual and sometimes frightening. They tended to recur so that if an individual initially had hallucinations while sniffing, he would continue to have them in later sessions. It is not known why some people have hallucinations while others do not.

One twelve-year-old boy described his experiences as 'something happening like God or the Devil or monsters' while a 15-year-old boy was convinced that he had become a headstone in the local cemetery. He gave a very fluent description of this 'dream' which recurred during his normal sniffing sessions in a wood. Other descriptions were given which included 'aeroplanes' and 'little green men with bats'. The 'auditory hallucination' does not refer to the buzzing in the ears which is a recognised feature of this type of intoxication and which has given rise to the term 'buzzed up on glue'. One young person referred to his hallucinations as music which he heard inside his head while another said he heard horrible things which he could not describe properly.

## Illusions

A few individuals, (8 per cent), who were seen during the stage of acute intoxication described what were really distortions of reality rather than hallucinations. Some described snakes writhing on the floors and walls when in fact what they were really seeing were patterns on carpets or wallpaper. In other cases, trees or poles were thought to be people standing up straight and failing to reply when addressed.

A 16-year-old boy, who was seen by the author on numerous occasions, made it his regular practice to sniff glue vapours for several hours each afternoon. Thereafter, with a very unco-ordinated gait, he proceeded to weave an erratic path across six lanes of traffic at the rush hour. Each time he did so, he was rescued by the police. His interpretation of events was always the same. He was, so he claimed, at Blackpool where he could see the illuminations (car lights), and listen to the sounds of the Pleasure Beach (the traffic). What he was doing was misinterpreting external stimuli and he was quite unable to accept that he might be at risk during the process.

Another somewhat atypical, but amusing incident concerns a boy who, while sniffing glue with his friends said, 'This is a terrible dream I'm having. I'm dreaming about the fuzz'. In this case he was not dreaming and the police had actually arrived but it is another example of how the division between reality and fantasy may become blurred when someone is intoxicated by solvents.

## Accidents and Incidents

The intoxication from solvent abuse causes impaired judgement, poor awareness of surroundings and lack of both muscle control and co-ordination. Hallucinations characterise some cases and illusions occur in a few. The combination of intoxication and illusions could have been expected to produce a large number of accidents among the 335 individuals seen over the nine-year period but in fact 328 never had an accident at any stage during the period of solvent abuse. Details of the accidents reported by the remaining seven (2 per cent of the total) are given in Table 6.1. All but one were in a group at the time, all had been involved in glue sniffing per se for some time and all required hospital treatment as a result of their accidents but none was seriously injured or died. No-one reported more than one accident.

No other serious mishaps were reported by the majority of those seen in the study. However, a 16-year-old boy who was seen in an acutely intoxicated state reported having suffered two cardiac arrests after sniffing glue on previous occasions but these experiences had not deterred him from continuing the practice on a long-term basis. His cardiac arrests had occurred when he was sniffing glue with friends and help had been obtained quickly. Two boys reported having received burn injuries from fires lit to heat the cans of glue and one said that he had been burned while holding his cigarette in one hand and the glue in the other. A further 24 individuals (7 per cent of the total), all male, had been implicated in incidents in which knives had been used to threaten family members, siblings or peer group rivals. However, since their judgement was impaired and their co-ordination poor owing to their state of intoxication, they inflicted no damage or injury except in one case in which a 14-year-old boy, when extremely intoxicated, took a knife to his baby brother of whom he was very jealous. Two others, who had been drinking alcohol as well as abusing solvents, were involved in incidents in which firearms were discharged but again there were no injuries.

Table 6.1: Accidents Reported by 335 Sniffers*

| Description of the accident | Injuries |
| --- | --- |
| Fall while intoxicated | Broken arm |
| Fall while intoxicated | Broken leg |
| Fall while intoxicated | Dislocated shoulder |
| Fall while intoxicated | Broken arm |
| Fall while intoxicated | Severe cuts to both hands by glass |
| Fall while intoxicated | Head injury |
| Road traffic accident - fell in front of moving car | Broken arm and leg Head injury |

* Total number of accidents was seven. All required hospital treatment.

A study of Glasgow hospital statistics for admissions in the period from 1980 to 1983 supports the author's findings that harmful incidents associated with solvent abuse are quite rare. Only

44 young people, aged from 11 to 18 years were admitted, most of them in a state of intoxication.[5] Of these, six were unconscious, five had met with accidents, one suffered a cardiac arrest and one was suffering from hypothermia after lying in the street for some time (Table 6.2).

Table 6.2: Solvent Abuse Admissions to Greater Glasgow Health Board Hospitals 1980-1983

| Reason for admission | Number of admissions |
|---|---|
| Intoxication | 31 (70%) |
| Accident | 5 (12%) |
| Coma | 6 (14%) |
| Cardiac arrest | 1 (2%) |
| Hypothermia | 1 (2%) |
| Total | 44 |

Coma

A very small proportion (3 per cent) of the 335 children had been admitted to hospital on a previous occasion in a state of coma caused by solvent abuse and another 14 per cent said that they had experienced blackouts but had not ended up in hospital. Most of these said that coma had occurred only once and a few stated that it had happened on two or three occasions (Figure 6.5). None said that they normally became unconscious during sessions. As far as could be determined from friends and parents, all of those who had experienced blackouts or coma were regularly involved in glue sniffing. Taking account of the total number of times these abusers had indulged, it would appear that the risk of coma is slight during any single glue sniffing session. Most of those who reported blackouts and all who had been admitted to hospital had been sniffing glue solvents from bags. Five had been using dry-cleaners or shoe conditioner.

Coma is known to be hazardous since it causes the loss of protective body reflexes and, if the coma deepens, breathing might stop. The most important risk is that something might happen to impede the breathing in which case the individual would die of asphyxia. For example, if he became unconscious and fell on his face, his air passages might become impeded or, if he fell into water, he might drown. Alternatively, if he fell on his back, he might develop asphyxia from some mechanical obstruction or, if he vomited, his impaired protective reflexes would fail to prevent the vomit from entering his lungs and suffocating him.

Figure 6.5: Coma Following Solvent Intoxication

Source: Reproduced by kind permission of the Royal Society for the Prevention of Accidents.


## Solvents

It has already been explained that it is not the products, such as glues, which are inhaled but some of the chemicals that they contain. Information from the manufacturers about the products indicates that the situation is far from simple since the chemicals present in glues and their proportions vary over the whole range of products. The same is true for cleaning substances and other products that might be abused. The different components which might be abused, along with some of the products containing them can be seen in Table AB.1

which was kindly supplied by the British Adhesives and Sealants Association. A simplified version of this information is given in Table AB.2

It can be seen from this appendix that the situation is complicated and that many solvents might be encountered. It is not always possible to tell from the type of product, for example an impact glue, which solvents are present and even for a given brand, the proportions of solvent may vary from time to time depending on the availability of the different raw materials used in its manufacture. During the 1970s, some manufacturers were very helpful about revealing which solvents were present in their products but others were not so forthcoming, perhaps because of the fear of competition.

In 1976, research was begun in the Department of Forensic Medicine at Glasgow University to develop a method of identifying the volatile chemicals present in different products. It was hoped to use the same or a similar method to detect these chemicals in the blood, urine or breath of individuals who had been abusing solvents. Blood samples were taken by the author from glue sniffers and these, along with samples from non-sniffing volunteers, were analysed in a machine using the relatively simple technique, gas chromatography. This method was tried out on samples from 50 referrals in 1976 and was found to work quickly and efficiently. Toluene was found to be the solvent whose vapours were most commonly abused but a test for the presence of other chemicals was carried out on each sample of blood in order to obtain the fullest details in each case.[6] This technique also proved to be a useful diagnostic tool since it made it possible to check for the presence of solvents in cases of coma or death if the diagnosis was uncertain or in cases where the abuse of solvents was suspected but not clinically proved.

Solvent Levels and Intoxication

Further development was considered necessary so that, instead of merely identifying the presence of a substance, it would be possible to measure the levels that were present in the body of someone who had been abusing solvents. This would make it possible to investigate the relationship between the degree of intoxication and the actual levels of these substances in the blood as has been done for alcohol. As a result, between October 1977 and July

1979, a special method using capillary column chromatography was developed to measure solvent levels in samples of blood. Samples were taken by doctors at police stations or the casualty departments of Glasgow hospitals from 82 young people who were suspected of being involved in glue sniffing sessions within the previous few hours. Samples of blood were also taken from 23 workers exposed to solvent vapours in the course of their employment. These samples were analysed at the Department of Forensic Medicine at Glasgow University.[7] In the cases where solvent abuse was suspected, full details about the state of the patient were also recorded along with information such as the presence of a smell on the breath, euphoria, any apparent degree of intoxication and comments about whether the patient was conscious or in a coma. In four of the cases, the patient was dead.

Comparison of the clinical state with the levels of solvents measured in this way made it possible to relate the symptoms to the blood levels. A summary of these results is given in Figure 6.6

Figure 6.6: The Relationship between Clinical State and Blood Level of Toluene.

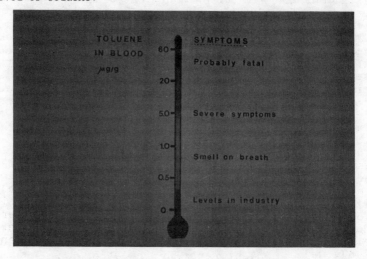

It can be seen that the first sign is the smell on the breath which can be detected at a level of 0.4 micrograms of solvent per gram of blood, followed at higher levels by intoxication, coma and finally death at levels above 10 micrograms per gram. It should also be noted that the industrial levels were markedly lower than those found in the solvent abusers.[8]

These analytical techniques have been useful in making the diagnosis of solvent abuse in difficult cases. However, in the majority of cases seen in Strathclyde, it was not difficult to establish the cause of intoxication or coma.

To summarise, the acute effects of solvent abuse were found to be very similar to those of alcoholic intoxication. There is some initial euphoria followed by depression of the central nervous system with blurring of vision, double vision, slurring of speech, staggering gait and eventually coma. Marked differences were also noted. Firstly, with solvent abuse, there is an extremely rapid onset of intoxication, usually within a few minutes, followed by an almost equally rapid recovery, usually within 30 to 60 minutes of the end of the session. Secondly, there is the marked chemical smell from the breath which is characteristic of the abuse of solvents. Finally, hallucinations and visual distortions are found in a proportion of the cases but are not a feature of acute alcoholic intoxication.

No specific treatment was required by the 355 cases of acute solvent abuse seen by the author. All were conscious when examined and none seemed to have come to any serious harm despite the potential risks associated with the practice.


The Psychological Effects

This section described the psychological symptoms associated with solvent abuse such as habituation, addiction, impairment of memory and concentration and underlying psychiatric illness. The available literature on each topic is reviewed and is followed by a description of the symptoms that were found in a sample of 788 young people who were personally seen by the author between 1975 and 1984.

This sample includes 335 people already mentioned as having initially been seen while acutely intoxicated. The remainder consisted of 453 individuals all of whom were referred by police, social workers, school nurses, teachers, general practitioners, psychiatrists and parents with the exception of a small group who were over the age of 16 and self-referred. Most, (90 per cent) had abused glue only, three had abused only butane and the remainder had inhaled the vapours from a wide range of products including cleaning fluids, nail polish remover, hair lacquer and fire extinguishers. The great majority seemed to be perfectly healthy young people. their ages ranged from 8 to 28 years but most were aged between 12 and 16. 101 (13 per cent) had been involved in solvent abuse on a regular basis for six months or more while the remainder had stopped. All were habitual sniffers who abused glue except one who preferred butane gas.

## Solvent Dependence and Addiction

When some drugs are taken over extended periods of time, the body becomes accustomed to their presence so that the effect of a given amount is reduced. This is called tolerance and means that the individual has to take a larger dose in order to achieve the same effect. It occurs more rapidly with drugs such as heroin than with others such as alcohol or cannabis. In the case of certain drugs, a person taking them may also develop a condition called dependence (commonly known as addiction). This has been defined as a condition with behavioural and other responses including a craving for the psychological effects of the drug or the need to take it in order to avoid the physical discomfort of withdrawal.

There is general agreement in the literature that repeated exposure to solvents causes the development of tolerance to those solvents.[4] Some American authors have stated that it can develop within three months of the commencement of weekly sniffing sessions.[1] Psychological dependence was also reported to be common and habitual sniffers in America found it hard to give up the practice unless a suitable alternative was available. Considerable doubt was expressed about physical addiction to solvents although some British and American psychiatrists reported that chronic sniffers experienced delirium tremens, irritability and headaches on withdrawal of solvents.[3,9,10] However, a recent study carried out in Canada of 24 individuals who had abused solvents repeatedly for two to ten years observed no withdrawal symptoms in any of its subjects after their admission to hospital.[11]

In Strathclyde, most of the 101 habitual sniffers had developed tolerance to the effects of solvents although there was an enormous variation in the amounts required by each individual. This ranged from two or three tubes weekly to four or five pints of adhesive daily. The individual who abused butane required seven or eight cans daily.

Physical symptoms following the withdrawal of solvents were seen in only one case, that of a 13-year-old male glue sniffer. This boy had been admitted to an assessment centre because of his delinquent behaviour and had been involved in solvent abuse for two and a half years, gradually increasing his consumption of glue (containing toluene) until it reached a total of three to four pints daily.[12] 36 hours after admission to the centre, he began to complain of abdominal cramps, aches in his limbs, nausea and vomiting. These symptoms persisted over the next five days and, in spite of daily examination by the author, no explanation for them could be found. On the fifth day, the boy remembered suffering similar symptoms on the only other occasion on which he had stopped sniffing glue for a few days. These symptoms were observed to continue for a further five days before gradually disappearing without any treatment. Although no other reason was found for these symptoms, it does not prove that they were due to physical withdrawal of the solvents. If these symptoms were due to physical withdrawal, then they are a very rare occurrence and do not require any treatment.

Only a few of the habitual sniffers described feelings of desperation about maintaining a source of supply for their habit and most did not feel very strongly about the matter. Twelve described the lengths to which they were prepared to go in order to acquire solvents. Some had broken out of their homes at night when their supply ran out and one had gone naked to a friend's house because his parents had taken away his clothes in an attempt to curb the habit. Most of these twelve people had stolen articles from their homes and sold them in order to support the habit and all of them admitted to having stolen goods from shops. It was clear that these twelve young people showed signs of psychological dependence but, apart from the one case already described, there were no signs of physical dependence.

## Psychiatric or Psychological Dysfunction

It has been mentioned in the literature that young people with emotional or psychiatric difficulties would be more likely to abuse solvents than those with no such problems.[4] This presumably means that the screening of individuals who abuse solvents would detect cases with underlying problems. In Strathclyde, some psychiatrists have stated that psychiatric illness may be an underlying feature of some solvent abusers while others in the field have not found this to be the case.[13,14]

Among the solvent abusers seen by the author, none of the sporadic or social users reported any psychological symptoms. However, among the habitual abusers, 14 reported persistent insomnia and recurring nightmares for several months while a further seven complained of nightmares only. These symptoms all developed after they had started to abuse solvents regularly. Another eight individuals complained of persistent depression or listlessness. All 29 were referred for psychiatric assessment. Eleven of these did not attend because their parents invariably found it impossible to keep the appointments, two were found to have reactive depression caused by family bereavements and the remainder were assessed as normal.

The possible impact of long-term exposure to solvent vapours on various brain functions such as concentration, decision-making and memory has been discussed in the literature, and investigated by a number of psychologists in America. In 1963, a study of 27 inhalant-abusing children and a group of similar non-abusing controls found no significant differences between the two groups when they were subjected to psychological tests.[15] A study in 1964 of 12 glue sniffers and 21 randomly selected controls again found no differences in performance results in tests of memory, attention, perception and concentration.[16] However, two other American studies indicated that solvent abusers showed impaired function when tested but, as one of the studies[17] involved only ten subjects, the small size of the sample could have given rise to large errors and it is not at all clear whether or not any of the subjects were screened for underlying psychiatric conditions which might have caused the impairment in the first place. The other study was of 75 youths all of whom had lengthy histories of solvent abuse. They were extensively investigated using tests of personality, intelligence, attention and memory.[18] The preliminary results showed that the performance of the abusers was worse than that of the controls and it was concluded that chronic solvent abusers might develop impairment.

In a recent study carried out in central Scotland, ten chronic solvent abusers and ten matched controls were compared and it was found that the solvent abuse group showed significant impairment in tests of memory, non-verbal intelligence, attention and concentration.[19] There were a number of weaknesses in this study. Firstly, the psychologist who carried out the tests knew to which group each individual belonged and this might have biased the results. Secondly, the sample was small and the result is therefore sensitive to the random variations that occur anyway between one person and the next. Finally, it was never confirmed that the sniffers had not indulged recently and although they reported that their last session had taken place ten days to six weeks before the tests, this was not verified. If any of these individuals had abused solvents more recently than that, residual intoxication could have caused impairment similar to that found but it would not prove the existence of long-term dysfunction of the brain. The results in themselves are very interesting and this study should be repeated using a larger sample with tests to discount the possibility of recent sniffing.

In the Strathclyde study of 788 solvent abusers seen by the author, twelve reported difficulty of concentration and memory. The mothers complained that their children seemed to be unable to concentrate on anything they did and that, when they were sent on errands, they often had to turn back because they could not remember where they were going or why. Because these symptoms are unusual at that age and because the mothers' descriptions were so vivid, all twelve were referred for psychological and psychiatric assessment. All were found to be normal and, since the tests discovered no impairment, the significance of the reported symptoms is therefore not understood.

To summarise, out of 788 solvent abusers seen by the author, only the 101 habitual sniffers reported any psychological symptoms. All had developed a degree of tolerance to solvents and some described the onset of headaches, nightmares and insomnia but none was found to have any measurable psychiatric disorder. In particular, the few who had complained of impaired memory and concentration were found to perform normally in tests. It is possible that the reported dysfunction of memory and concentration was entirely due to recent episodes of acute intoxication and that at the time of testing they had not been indulging sufficiently recently to be impaired.

The extent of all the other problems in the lives of these chronic abusers was apparent and most were in trouble with their parents because of disruptive behaviour at home. They were frequently intoxicated by solvents and it seemed that this intoxication was a reaction to circumstances which they found to be stressful. It is likely that they were psychologically dependent in the sense of needing to be intoxicated in order to cope with their lives and it would be logical to conclude that they were more susceptible to the abuse of other intoxicating substances than most people. The likely result of the intoxication would be to aggravate the situation because their befuddled minds would be unable to deal with problems and resolve difficulties. It seems very probable that such individuals will remain emotionally immature unless they can be helped to face up to their problems, painful though this might prove to be for them. If such assistance is not forthcoming, they will continue to depend on a chemical solution to the problems in their lives.


The Physical Effects

Information about physical effects caused by solvent abuse has appeared in the literature from time to time. The reports have often been contradictory since, on the one hand, some investigators have stated categorically that no physical damage was detected among solvent abusers,[1,20] while others believe strongly that damage could be caused in that way. The information about possible damage reported throughout the world has been mainly in the form of isolated case reports and, until recently, no large scale studies of toxic effects among solvent abusers had been reported. It is quite clear from the literature that damage to organ systems has indeed occurred in certain individuals who were involved in solvent abuse. What is much less clear and what continues to cause confusion is that mishaps are rare, the mechanism for damage is not well understood and there may be multiple associated factors in each case which make interpretation difficult.

As has been described earlier, the solvents enter the bloodstream by way of the lungs, are carried round the body and have a particular affinity for brain fats. They are eliminated by being exhaled, by being broken down in the liver or by being excreted via the kidneys. The direct actions of these substances on the body are not well known but it seems likely that the organs which are most vulnerable to damage are the liver, kidneys and brain.

Despite the enormous numbers of people who have been involved in solvent abuse since the 1960s, there are only about 30 case reports in world literature relating to impairment of liver or kidney function in solvent abusers.

Trichloroethylene and trichloroethane, substances found in dry-cleaning fluids, were found to be implicated in a few cases of acute liver and/or kidney damage. A 15-year-old boy was admitted to a New York hospital in 1968 with jaundice. He was said to have been healthy prior to this episode but had regularly abused glues, amphetamines, heroin, cocaine and cannabis. He denied drinking alcohol. Ten months before his admission to hospital, he had sniffed trichloroethylene fumes from cleaning fluid on one occasion only and had suffered a severe headache immediately afterwards. During the month prior to admission, he had sniffed glue solvents but had not used any other drugs. Six days before admission, he began to sniff trichloroethylene vapour and continued to do so for three days. After this time he developed jaundice and was admitted to hospital. He was found to have damaged his liver but subsequently made a good recovery and was discharged after thirteen days.

There are four other case reports from New York and Philadelphia of individuals, aged between 15 and 22, all of whom developed dysfunction of liver and kidneys following exposure to trichloroethylene in cleaning fluids. These reactions were thought to be the toxic effects of the exposure. However, it was discovered that the 22-year-old had suffered from viral hepatitis six months before he started sniffing trichloroethylene and, in addition, his consumption of alcohol had been high for some months before his admission to hospital. He developed both liver and kidney damage and died on

the sixth day after admission to hospital. The
remaining three persons had been involved in the
abuse of other substances such as alcohol,
amphetamines or barbiturates and all recovered from
their episodes of acute liver and kidney damage so
that they were able to leave hospital after two or
three weeks.[21,22]

In New York in 1969, a study was carried out
of ten teenagers aged 12 to 16 who had sniffed spot
remover containing trichloroethylene and trichloroethane.[23] No details were given in the report about
the extent of the sniffing. Blood tests revealed no
abnormalities in five cases but the other five had
abnormal liver function tests, four of them
developing jaundice within one week of exposure to
the spot remover. One developed coma because of the
severity of the liver damage and two developed
kidney dysfunction, one to the point of renal
failure. However, all eventually recovered.

In 1963, six individuals in Los Angeles
developed bone marrow depression apparently after
glue sniffing. Before this occurred, five had
sickle cell disease, a blood disorder that affects
certain ethnic groups including negroes, but all
made a rapid recover after the glue sniffing was
discontinued. The sixth person, who had previously
been normal, died from the bone marrow depression.[24]
It was thought that the agent responsible in these
cases for the bone marrow depression was benzene
which is known to be highly toxic and is no longer
used in adhesives. No other cases of bone marrow
depression have been reported in relation to
solvent abuse.

In 1971, a case report appeared in the British
Medical Journal about a 19-year-old youth who had
been admitted to hospital in Birmingham suffering
from acute renal failure. He had been involved in
glue sniffing for three years and, during that
time, had sometimes noticed that he failed to
produce urine for anything up to three days after
sniffing. On the day of his admission to hospital,
he had been sniffing a toluene-containing liquid
cleaner, and had consumed three pints of beer.
After admission to hospital, he was still unable to
pass urine and was given dialysis treatment. He
also developed liver dysfunction but recovered from
both the liver and kidney problems after six weeks.
When he was seen at the outpatient department six
months later he was well and no longer involved in
glue sniffing.[25]

Another case report from Australia appeared in

1981 and involved a 20-year-old man who was admitted to the Royal Adelaide Hospital with acute renal failure. Until this illness, he had been well. He had been sniffing a toluene-containing glue, once or twice per week throughout the previous nine months. During the week before his admission he had felt generally unwell and his urine output had been significantly reduced. On the day before admission, he had sniffed glue from a small plastic bag as was his custom. There appeared to be no history of any contact with toxic substances other than those in glue. The patient required dialysis treatment but in spite of this and three renal biopsies he failed to produce urine for 70 days after admission to hospital. His illness was thought to be due to the effect of toluene on his kidneys but the final outcome of this case is unknown.[26]

Between 1979 and 1984 there were twelve other case reports[27,28,29] from Miami, Portland in Oregon and Oklahoma City from departments of medicine, urology and nephrology. The twelve individuals reported had been involved in the sniffing of toluene from glues, paint thinners, transmission fluid and paints. All showed disturbances of the acid-base balance of the body which was thought to have been secondary to the toxic effect of toluene on the kidneys. One died,[27] one continued to have persistent problems with his metabolism for 18 months but denied that he was still actively involved in paint sniffing.[29] The remaining ten patients made rapid recoveries following intravenous fluid therapy in hospital.

Some observations on these reports are obviously desirable to see if they reveal some overall pattern in what initially seems to be a confusing picture. It is also necessary to discuss whether or not any of these reports is relevant to the practice of solvent abuse existing at present in this country.

The bone marrow depression reported in six cases following the sniffing of a benzene-containing glue has not recurred since that occasion. This can be explained by the fact that benzene, which is known to be highly toxic and believed to be the relevant factor in these cases, is no longer used in glues. This adverse reaction has not been reported in relation to any other solvent and it would seem unlikely to recur.

Toxic effects on the liver and kidneys were reported in 24 cases in relation to products

containing toluene, trichloroethylene and trichloroethane. Even if these were solely due to the abuse
of solvents, the number involved is still tiny when
compared with the overall numbers involved in the
abuse of products containing these chemicals. Even
in the 24 cases already described, the case against
solvent abuse has not been proved since four of the
people involved were known to have abused other
drugs and relevant drug information was not
available for some of the others. One patient had
suffered from viral hepatitis six months before his
exposure to solvents and, in addition, had a heavy
alcohol consumption. The combination of a liver
recovering from infective damage and heavy alcohol
consumption would make the liver much more
vulnerable to further damage and the trichloroethylene
cannot therefore be said to be the only cause of
the damage.

In the remaining 19 cases where there is no
known alternative cause for the damage, the
mechanism for the toxicity is not clear. The length
of individual exposure to solvents in each of these
cases is not known precisely but it would not seem
to have been extensive in most cases and there
could be considerable variation overall. It is
possible that the effects seen were an unusual or
even rare reaction in a few individuals who might
not have been subjected to much exposure but who
were particularly susceptible in some way to these
chemicals. This type of hypersensitivity reaction
has also been seen in relation to drugs used
medicinally. Most people experience no adverse
reactions but sometimes a very few people may
experience them. This could happen after very
little exposure or it could occur suddenly and
unexpectedly after considerable exposure which
previously did not cause any problems.[30] This would
seem to apply to the 19 cases studied since the
patterns are similar and it is possible that these
individuals were just unlucky in having an unusual
sensitivity to these solvents. Although adverse
reactions are rare, two of the individuals involved
died and another failed to regain kidney function
so these cases are still important. It is hoped
that they will continue to be reported, as is done
in the case of medicines, so that any overall
pattern of reactions can be fully understood.

Adverse reactions involving the brain have
also been reported. A case was reported in 1978
from the University of Washington in which a young
man who had been sniffing gasoline for many years

was found to have unco-ordinated ataxic gait, tremor of limbs and signs of dementia. He subsequently died.[31] Similar symptoms were reported from New Mexico in 1977 in a 14-year-old girl who had been sniffing gasoline for two years.[32] In Winnipeg between 1975 and 1976, 46 children out of 50 seen at a childrens' centre showed signs of damage to the central nervous system due to repeated gasoline sniffing over a period of six months to five years.[33] It was not clear initially in these cases involving gasoline whether the damage to the central nervous system was caused by the volatile chemicals present in the petrol or by the tetra-ethyl-lead which is added as an anti-knock agent. Since the lead level in the bodies of these children was high and treatment for lead poisoning caused the symptoms to disappear in all cases except one, it would seem reasonable to conclude that the lead was the agent causing this reaction.

There have also been some reports linking damage to the solvent n-hexane. This substance is widely used in Japan in printing and cleaning processes and industrial workers who have been continuously exposed to it have sometimes developed disorders of vision and dysfunction of the limbs. Solvent abuse involving n-hexane seems to have been uncommon but there is a report of a 19-year-old man who had been sniffing glue (containing toluene and other petroleum distillates but not n-hexane) for five years, during which time he remained in good health. When he switched to a brand containing n-hexane, his weight fell by 38 pounds within two months and he developed pain, tingling and weakness in both legs.[34] Soon, he was unable to sit or stand without support. When he stopped sniffing glue, his weakness seemed to grow worse initially but when he was seen one year later he was much improved and able to walk although he still had a degree of impairment.

There is a similar case report of a 22-year-old who was seen at the University of Pennsylvania. He had a ten year history of glue sniffing and, like the previous case, was well until he started to sniff a glue containing n-hexane. Again, within a month, he noted weight loss and weakness in both legs but retained his ability to walk. After discharge from hospital, he did not stop sniffing glues but used only those without n-hexane. When he was seen one year after the onset of his illness his nervous system was

undamaged.[35] Another similar case concerned a
29-year-old glue sniffer who developed corresponding
symptoms when he switched to glues containing
n-hexane and ended up confined to a wheelchair.[36]
The neuropathy in all these cases was said to have
characteristic features which could be seen in
special nerve conduction tests.

It is worthy of note that, in spite of long
histories of heavy solvent abuse, none of these
individuals had any symptoms before the abuse of
n-hexane and then developed dysfunction of the
nervous system. It is not known how many people
were exposed to n-hexane in the course of their
solvent abuse but it seems clear that it can
produce toxic effects in some susceptible individuals
and also that the exposure need not be large or
prolonged.

It is also interesting to note that, in all
the preceding case histories, the long exposure to
toluene did not appear to cause any adverse
symptoms and this seems to be common. For example,
a case was reported in 1963 of a man who had abused
toluene for ten years and whose nervous system was
found to be normal.[37] However, that does not mean
that there are no reports of adverse reactions of
the nervous system to toluene.

In 1961, a psychiatrist in California reported
a habitual sniffer who showed signs of brain
dysfunction after six years of repeated and
deliberate exposure to toluene. The balance
mechanism of the body was found to be impaired, he
had a tremor of both hands and feet and a
staggering gait when walking. At first, he was
thought to have multiple sclerosis or a familial
disorder of the nervous system but these were later
excluded. It was then thought that his symptoms
were signs of irreversible degeneration of brain
tissue following prolonged exposure to toluene.[38]
In his paper, Dr. Grabski said, 'psychiatrists will
undoubtedly see more and more patients who have
sought refuge from their personality disorders
through the inhalation of solvents and may overlook
the serious toxic effects of these drugs'. Despite
warnings, the patient continued to abuse solvents
over the years. On one occasion, he could not
obtain toluene and turned to carbon tetrachloride
although he knew it was harmful. He was subsequently
admitted to hospital with acute liver poisoning.
After he had recovered from this acute upset, his
central nervous system was examined again during
the next six months. It was found that his

electroencephalogram (EEG) showed signs suggesting brain damage.[39] Psychological tests did not find any conclusive evidence of organic mental deterioration although he still had tremor of the hands and some difficulty in walking. This case seems to provide evidence that prolonged exposure to toluene can greatly impair function of the nervous system but there seems to be no evidence of structural damage.

In 1978, a girl of 18 was admitted to a Swedish hospital for investigation of dysfunction of the nervous system. She was unsteady on her feet, had slurred speech, unco-ordinated ataxic gait, nystagmus and a loss of visual acuity in both eyes. She had a six year history of habitually inhaling toluene vapour. She had been unemployed during the previous six months so that she had been inhaling its vapour more than usual. There was no history of other drug abuse or of excessive alcohol abuse. After five weeks in hospital, she showed a marked improvement but still had some impairment of function. Three months later, during which time she had not abused toluene, she was found to have recovered perfect function of her nervous system and her visual acuity had improved.[40]

Another report, from Japan, concerned a 27-year-old male who was admitted to hospital in 1978 with tremor and disorders of balance. He had been habituated to glue sniffing for ten years with a very heavy daily exposure to toluene during the previous six months. Earlier, he had been aware of a tremor of both arms and noticed that it vanished when he sniffed toluene. This continued for five months but eventually the tremors failed to disappear when he sniffed toluene. He developed a tremor of his neck which was followed shortly afterwards by lack of co-ordination and unsteadiness when walking. Tests on his brain showed atrophy of brain tissue.[41]

In 1981, two more cases were reported from Chicago. The first was that of a 28-year-old man who was referred from a neurology clinic for a psychiatric opinion. The patient showed coarse tremors, staggering gait and slurred speech. There was no family history of neurological disease but he did have a history of occasional substance abuse involving heroin, LSD, alcohol and a variety of pills. He had been abusing toluene for fourteen years to the point where his life began to centre round his inhalation of toluene to the exclusion of all other substances. After six years of toluene

139

abuse, he noticed that his hands shook but found that he could stop the tremor by inhaling more toluene. This was effective for two years but then, after a total of eight years of involvement with toluene, he developed a tremor of his upper limbs which was so severe that he could not hold objects. At the same time he experienced more difficulty in walking and his vision became blurred. These problems became worse during the next five years and his weight dropped dramatically. He sought medical aid claiming that he had not abused solvents for five months and was therefore annoyed to find that the tremors had not stopped. On examination, he was found to have staggering gait, lack of co-ordination and tremors of the arms, legs, head and neck. Psychological examination found him to be mentally defective with an IQ of 62. A brain scan showed loss of brain tissue.[42]

The second case from Chicago, reported in the same paper, concerned a 30-year-old man who was brought to the hospital by the police following an acute episode of solvent abuse. He was having hallucinations with a religious theme and believed that he was speaking to God and Jesus Christ. He had sniffed glue containing toluene since he was twelve and had at times indulged in glue sniffing binges, using six or seven tubes in one session, followed by periods of abstinence. He was thought to suffer from paranoid schizophrenia and was one of eleven children many of whom were schizophrenic or severely mentally retarded. Despite the prolonged exposure to toluene he was found to have only mildly impaired function of the nervous system but, before further tests could be carried out, he was lost to follow-up.

In 1983, there was a report from Tennessee regarding a 27-year-old man who developed brain atrophy during a period of five years in which he was involved in extensive glue sniffing. He also developed deafness and blindness for which no cause other than the abuse of glue could be found. When he was initially seen in 1976, he had been sniffing glue from a bag for several months and had slurred speech and a staggering gait. The results of his brain scan were normal as were the tests for structural damage of the brain. Screening for other drugs indicated that none had been abused recently. After a week without toluene, the abnormalities gradually improved. Two years later, after continued abuse of toluene, he again began to develop impaired vision and hearing. These symptoms progessed and when he was examined in 1981, his optic discs had atrophied, he had marked loss of hearing and a brain scan revealed a loss of tissue which was not seen five years before.[43]

There is therefore evidence that long-term abuse of toluene is associated in some cases with dysfunction of the nervous system. All the individuals in the cases described had been involved in habitual solvent abuse for 5 to 14 years but in some cases the evidence is weakened by other factors. Some had abused other drugs and alcohol so there could be some doubt about the integrity of their nervous systems before starting toluene abuse. One of them may have been schizophrenic and another was not only mentally defective but was also borderline in many aspects of his life.

The three cases in which brain scans showed loss of brain tissue provide the strongest evidence for associated brain damage, particularly the case in which there had been a normal scan five years previously. Another case showed severely impaired brain function but no signs of structural damage. These do suggest that the abuse of toluene is implicated, directly or indirectly, in producing brain damage. Even so, the mechanism might be complicated and there could be several additional factors such as differing individual susceptibilities to toxic substances, lack of oxygen in the brain during solvent abuse, the involvement with different solvents or the effects of multidrug use. All the individuals in these cases lost weight dramatically so malnutrition might also be a factor. In contrast to these examples of severe damage, the other three cases showed impairment but returned to normal in three months, one showed minimal impairment and the third showed no impairment even after ten years of abuse of toluene.

Apart from these individual case studies of people who requested medical aid because of problems with their nervous system, there is additional information about possible brain damage from studies conducted with groups of solvent abusers. A study in 1982 from Louisville, Kentucky, involved 42 white solvent abusers all of whom had inhaled the fumes from toluene. Eleven of them were selected for tests of the nervous system on account of symptoms such as tremors, slow speech or tingling in parts of the body. They were aged from 15 to 31 years. None gave a history of chronic substance abuse other than with toluene and none had a family history of degenerative disease of the nervous system. The weight of each was within 10 per cent of the standard weight for his height. When brain scans were carried out, five were found to be normal and six showed degeneration of the brain tissue which was described as mild in four cases and mild to moderate in the other two. All had been abusing solvents for ten years or more. It is not known whether the structural damage to the brain found in these six individuals was reversible or not.[44]

Another recent study in 1983 described 24 habitual solvent abusers who were examined during a two week period in hospital to determine if they had any impairment of function of the nervous system or any structural brain damage. Their ages ranged from 15 to 34 and they had been involved with the abuse of solvents for two and a half to eleven years. In order to qualify for inclusion in the study, each had to have reported daily use of solvents for a least one year and they had to be intoxicated on the day of admission. Most were very thin but there was no laboratory evidence of malnutrition. All were given a general physical and neurological examination with chest X-rays, EEGs, blood tests and psychological tests. Not all of these habitual abusers showed significant abnormalities of the nervous system, particularly with respect to tremor and ataxic gait.[11] Fifteen were classified as impaired and the remaining nine as unimpaired. Only eleven stayed in hospital for the full two weeks. It was concluded that long-term abuse of toluene was associated in some users with dysfunction of the brain, particularly of balance control, and with intellectual and memory impairment. These defects were accompanied by a marked loss of brain tissue. No improvement in function was detected during the two weeks of the study but it was suggested that a study using a larger sample and conducted for a longer period might serve to determine if the function could be restored and whether the structural abnormalities might be reversible. This study did not find any relationship between dosage and damage since some of the individuals who were the heaviest abusers had no functional impairment while the most severe impairment did not always occur among the heaviest abusers.

The problems of identifying the factors involved in the toxic reactions seen in the brains of certain solvent abusers remain unsolved. In some cases, it may have been due to n-hexane or lead but the determining factors involved in relation to toluene are not clear. These could be personal factors such as individual genetic susceptibility or environmental factors such as malnutrition, as is seen in those whose lives revolve around the abuse of solvents. In these cases where impairment of brain function is found, some recover and some do not. A number of cases of actual loss of brain tissue have been found and it is not clear whether this is reversible

There is certainly circumstantial evidence linking toluene abuse to functional impairment and structural damage to the brain. However, the direct toxicity of toluene on the brain is not proved but neither is it refuted. At present, this situation is an obvious case for the Scottish legal verdict of 'not proven' and will remain so until larger, better controlled prospective studies can establish, beyond all reasonable doubt, a verdict of guilty or not guilty.


The Strathclyde Study.
The 788 individuals seen in the Strathclyde study were interviewed by the author, their medical histories noted and any medical problems recorded. All were given a general medical examination which included an examination of the central nervous system and the taking of blood samples to check for any liver or kidney abnormalities. If required, X-rays could be taken. Control samples of blood were also obtained from 400 volunteers in an assessment centre who had not been involved in solvent abuse. This was necessary since the values for some tests of blood from normal adolescents are markedly different from those for normal adults and these values for healthy young people were not well known at the time. All blood tests were carried out in a local hospital laboratory.

Medical histories revealed that four of the children suffered from bronchial asthma but had never required hospitalisation and were not currently taking medication. Another two had been admitted to hospital as infants because of convulsions but had not had any problems since then. One individual suffered from sickle cell anaemia. One child had a history of urinary tract infections which had required hospitalisation and treatment at the outpatient department. Apart from these problems, the medical histories revealed nothing significant and, in general, the members of the group were in excellent health.

Two children had been troubled by nosebleeds since starting solvent abuse but there did not seem to be any correlation between the sniffing sessions and the nosebleeds. Six of the 101 habitual sniffers complained of pains in the front of the chest but nothing was found on physical examination or on X-ray examination so the significance of this is not understood. 15 of the habitual sniffers had lost appetite and weight since their involvement in the practice. This weight loss was up to ten pounds over a period of six months in some cases. Appetites were restored and weight loss stopped when the individuals gave up abusing solvents.

Examinations of the central nervous systems revealed a minor upset of the balance mechanism of the brain in a 13-year-old boy who was a habitual sniffer using four or five pints of glue per day. This caused the author to refer him to a consultant paediatrician who confirmed the findings. The symptoms disappeared within ten days after the boy stopped glue sniffing and no other treatment was required. The other 787 cases showed no abnormalities of the nervous system.

General physical examination revealed no significant abnormalities in most cases. The children with bronchial asthma were asymptomatic when seen and the child with sickle cell anaemia was well so it was clear that glue sniffing had not affected these conditons. In eight of the glue sniffers, a residual effect of the practice was found in the form of 'glue sniffer's rash' which occurs only in the case of habitual sniffers who abuse glue. It was thought to result from repeated application of a plastic bag to the nose and mouth. It resembled acne vulgaris but disappeared when the sniffing ceased (Figure 6.7). As it develops only at a late stage of habitual glue sniffing and then only in a few of these cases, it is not useful as an early diagnostic sign.

Blood tests were carried out to detect any abnormalities of the liver or kidneys which might not show up in the physical examination. A whole range of tests of kidney and liver functions were carried out on each sample of blood. In all but two of the cases, the results were within the normal range for the age and sex of the individual concerned. Liver upsets were found in the two remaining cases but both were due to infection with hepatitis A virus. No abnormalities of liver or kidneys which could be directly associated with solvent abuse were detected.

Figure 6.7: Glue Sniffer's Rash

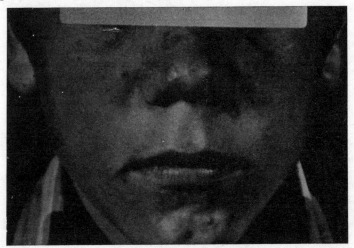

Source: Reproduced by kind permission of John Wright and Sons Ltd.,

To summarise all these results, no serious abnormalities which could be directly associated with solvent abuse were found in a sample of 788 young people which included 101 habitual abusers and most seemed to be physically healthy young people.

Four other individuals are known to have been admitted to Glasgow hospitals with physical symptoms which were thought to be conncected with solvent abuse. They were not part of the study just described but all four were seen and examined by the author.

A 13-year-old boy was admitted to hospital in May 1976 after an episode of glue sniffing. On admission, he had nausea, vomiting and right-sided abdominal pain and was noted to have jaundice. He gave a history of sniffing a toluene-containing glue daily for almost a year. He developed signs of acute liver and kidney dysfunction which returned to normal within twelve days. No evidence was found of infection by hepatitis virus and it is possible that this episode was a bizarre reaction to toluene or some other constituent in the glue. It is also possible that he had some infective process that was not detected during his stay in hospital.[45]

In 1981, a 14-year-old boy presented to his general practitioner with a 24 hour history of a sore throat and was prescribed an antibiotic. Next, day, he developed loin pains, frequently passed urine which contained blood and, as a result, was admitted to hospital. When his case history was taken, it was found that he had abused solvents for two years and had required half a pint of adhesive daily for eight months. After three weeks of abstinence, he had sniffed the vapour from one pint of glue daily for three consecutive days before his admission to hospital. When he was in hospital, his kidneys produced very little urine and he became rather puffy, but, after his fluid intake was restricted,the urine output began to improve. All the tests of kidney function returned to normal in four weeks. Although he was warned not to sniff glue again, he did so on two occasions and, each time, he experienced a recurrence of loin pain and passed blood in his urine. This case clearly demonstrates a reversible damage to kidneys probably due to toluene or some other chemical in the glue since the damage occurred only on those occasions when the substance was taken.[46]

In both these cases, one of liver and one of kidney dysfunction, the damage was reversible and may have been caused by bizarre hypersensitivity reactions in the individuals concerned. The following two cases involve brain dysfunction related to solvent abuse.

A 15-year-old boy was admitted to hospital in Glasgow in 1978 following four major epileptic fits. On admission, he was unconscious and afterwards continued to have frequent convulsions which were difficult to control. As a consequence of this, he was fed intravenously and put on a mechanical ventilator. There were no clues to the diagnosis in this case. The boy had experienced convulsions as a baby but not subsequently. Investigations, including a brain scan, skull and chest X-rays revealed no abnormalities and two brain biopsies were carried out. Following an anonymous telephone call to say that the boy had been involved in glue sniffing, the brain biopsy and blood samples were tested again and found to show high levels of toluene and a diagnosis of status epilepticus secondary to glue sniffing was made.[47] Nine months after this episode, although the boy was out of hospital, he was still having frequent fits. It was thought that, in this case, the convulsions were triggered in a vulnerable brain by the acute effects of glue sniffing.[48]

An eleven-year-old boy was admitted to a hospital in Glasgow with a week-old history of headache, vomiting, abnormal behaviour, slurred speech and unsteady gait. The medical history and family background gave no explanation for this. There was no known recent contact with infection and he denied any exposure to drugs or toxic agents. On examination, he was found to have nystagmus, severe ataxic gait with tremor and inco-ordination of the limbs. All tests, including a brain scan, skull X-ray and blood counts, were normal. On the third day, the possibility of a toxic reaction was considered and his blood was found to contain toluene. It was later discovered that he had been sniffing glue for several months. He improved somewhat during the next three weeks but, when he was seen at the outpatient clinic one year later he still had severe dysfunction of balance and gait and it is possible that he had sustained some long-term damage. Although blood tests for toluene were negative at this visit to the clinic, this does not necessarily prove that he had stopped sniffing glue so these residual abnormalities might be due to continued exposure to toluene.[8]

Nothing was known about this boy before he presented at the age of eleven. The extent of his exposure to glue sniffing was not specified and the exact cause of the dysfunction remains unknown. It is likely that individual susceptibility of a vulnerable nervous system to the toluene or the lack of oxygen while sniffing could play a major role in the development of the dysfunction. No structural damage was detected by the tests but the boy's function in relation to walking, balance and co-ordination was severely impaired. This case should be followed up to determine the ultimate outcome.

From the author's study of 788 individual glue her, it is clear that the risk of developing any impairment due to solvent abuse is small. When it does occur, there are many factors such as lack of oxygen or individual susceptibility which might act singly or in combination making it impossible to predict who might be at risk.


## The Deaths

Although it is still possible for uncertainties to remain about the toxicity of deliberate solvent abuse, there can be no doubt about the deaths which are associated with the practice. These have been reported from Japan, Finland, Denmark, Sweden and America.[2,4,49,50] Factors influencing the occurrence of death were the toxicity of the substance abused, dangerous methods of abuse or hazardous locations such as caves and isolated places where accidents were more likely to occur. Another factor reported in the literature was that of physical activity while intoxicated.

In 1977, the author, being aware of deaths in Strathclyde, but not initially of others elsewhere in Britain, undertook a study of deaths occurring between January 1970 and January 1977. It was found that there were 45 deaths relating to solvent abuse in Britain during that period.[51] Almost all were male and the ages ranged from 11 to 32.

Since then, a more detailed and extensive study of solvent abuse deaths in Britain has been undertaken in London.[52] Between 1971 and 1983, 282 deaths are known to have occurred at ages which ranged from 11 to 76 but 72 per cent of these involved people aged under 20 and 95 per cent were male. In 1983, 2 per cent of all deaths of males aged between 10 and 19 were attributable to solvent abuse. All areas of Britain were said to be represented with the highest rates occurring in Scotland and in urban areas. Deaths were found to be due to direct toxic effects in 51 per cent of the cases, mechanical obstruction of air passages in 21 per cent, inhalation of vomit in 18 per cent and injury in 11 per cent. The substances abused were found to be glue solvents (27 per cent), aerosols (17 per cent), gas fuels (24 per cent), and other volatile substances (31 per cent). Death was more likely when the individuals were sniffing alone (71 per cent) and occurred most frequently at home (45 per cent) or in a public place (29 per cent).

In Strathclyde, between January 1970 and December 1984, 41 deaths are known to have occurred in association with solvent abuse. The individuals were aged from 13 to 26 years and all but two were male. The pattern of deaths is similar to that found in the national survey with approximately 50 per cent of the cases involving direct toxic effects and the others being due to obstruction of airways, inhalation of vomit and injury. Glue solvents were involved in 29 per cent of the cases, aerosols in 12 per cent, butane or propane gas in 32 per cent and other substances in the remaining 26 per cent (Table 6.3).

Table 6.3: Deaths from Solvent Abuse in Strathclyde 1970-1984

| Substance abused | Number of deaths |
| --- | --- |
| Glue solvents | 12 (29%) |
| Aerosols | 5 (12%) |
| Butane or propane fuel | 13 (32%) |
| Other substances | 11 (26%) |
| Total | 41 |

This is in direct contrast to the experience of the author and others dealing with solvent abusers. It has been found that most known abusers are involved with glues and not with the other substances and yet glue solvent deaths were only 29 per cent of the total. This apparent contradiction must mean either that there are many individuals involved in the abuse of these other substances who are not seen for some reason or that the abuse of these substances is much less common than that of glue but much more likely to prove fatal. The author believes from her long experience of solvent abuse that the latter explanation is more likely and that the misuse of products other than glues is much more hazardous either because the substances themselves are more toxic or because the techniques used with them are considerably more dangerous.
    While there can be no remaining doubts about deaths related to solvent abuse, it is important to view the mortality statistics within a wider perspective. A study of deaths in Glasgow between 1980 and 1983 revealed that among those from 10 to 19 years the number of deaths associated with

solvent abuse were less than half of those from acute alcoholic poisoning and only 10 per cent of all accidental deaths recorded.[5]

Considering the relevant factors such as the immediate availability of solvent products and the thousands of teenagers likely to have experimented with their intoxicating vapours, it was reassuring to discover that so few deaths linked with the practice had occurred in Strathclyde since 1970. Undoubtedly, the most disturbing factor of the entire problem is that the adverse effects, particularly deaths, occur unpredictably and affect the young people of a community.

REFERENCES

1. Press, E. and Done, A.K. (1967), 'Solvent sniffing', Paediatrics, 39(4), 451-61 and 611-22.
2. Bass, M. (1970), 'Sudden sniffing death', Journal of the American Medical Association, 212(12), 2075-9.
3. Wyse, D.G. (1973), 'Deliberate inhalation of volatile hydrocarbons', Canadian Medical Association Journal, 108, 71-4.
4. Cohen, S. (1973), 'The volatile solvents', Public Health Reviews, 2(2), 185-214.
5. Greater Glasgow Health Board (1985), Information Services, personal communication.
6. Oliver, J.S. and Watson, J.M. (1977), 'Abuse of solvents "for kicks": a review of 50 cases', The Lancet, 1(8002), 84-6.
7. Oliver, J.S. and Watson, J.M. (1981), 'Analytical techniques in solvent abuse', Scottish Hospital Endowments Trust Grant HERT 516. Final Report, 1981, pp. 309-12.
8. King, M.D., Day, R.E., Oliver, J.S., and Watson, J.M. (1981), 'Solvent encephalopathy', British Medical Journal, 283, 663-4.
9. Crooke, S.T. (1972), 'Solvent inhalation', Texas Medicine, 68, 67-9.
10. Merry, J. and Zachariadis, N. (1962), 'Addiction to glue sniffing', British Medical Journal, 2, 1448.
11. Fornazzari, L., Wilkinson, D.A., Kapier, B.M. and Carlen P.L. (1983), 'Cerebellar, cortical and functional impairment in toluene abusers', Acta Neurol.Scand.,67, 319-29.
12. Watson, J.M. (1979), 'Glue sniffing: two case reports', The Practitioner, 222, 845-7.
13. Masterton, G. (1975), 'The management of solvent abuse', Journal of Adolescence, 2, 65-75.
14. Misra, P. (1985), 'Solvent Abuse Clinic', personal communication.
15. Massengale, O.N., Glaser, H.H., Le Lievere, R.E., Dodds, J.B. and Klock, M.E. (1963), 'Physical and psychologic factors in glue sniffing', New England Journal of Medicine, 269(25), 1340-4.
16. Dodds, J. and Santostefano, S. (1964), 'A comparison of the cognitive functioning of glue sniffers and non-sniffers', Journal of Paediatrics, 64(4), 565-70.
17. Bigler, E.D. (1979), 'Neuropsychological evaluation of adolescent patients hospitalised with chronic inhalant abuse', Clinical Neuropsychology, 1(1), 8-12.

18. Berry, G.J., Heaton R.K. and Kirby, M.W. (1977), 'Neuropsychological deficits of chronic inhalant abusers', in Ruemack, B.H. and Temple, A.R. (eds). Management of the poisoned patient, pp. 9-31, Princeton Press, Science Press.

19. Allison, W.M. and Jerrom, D.W.A. (1984), 'Glue sniffing: a pilot study of the cognitive effects of long-term use', International Journal of the Addictions, 19(4), 453-8.

20. Barman, M.L., Sigel, N.B., Beedle, D.B. and Larson, R.K. (1964), 'Acute and chronic effects of glue sniffing', California Medicine, 100, 19-22.

21. Baerg, R.D. and Kimberg, D.V. (1970), 'Centrilobular necrosis and acute renal failure in "solvent sniffers"', Annals of Internal Medicine, 73, 713-20.

22. Clearfield, H.R. (1970), 'Hepatorenal toxicity from sniffing spot-remover (trichloroethylene)', American Journal of Digestive Disorders, 15(9), 851-6.

23. Litt, I.F. and Cohen, M.E. (1969), 'Danger ..... vapour harmful', New England Journal of Medicine, 281(10), 543-4.

24. Powars, D. (1965), 'Aplastic anaemia secondary to glue sniffing', New England Journal of Medicine, 273(13), 700-2.

25. O'Brien, E.T., Yeoman, W.B. and Hobby, J.A.E. (1971), 'Hepatorenal damage from toluene in a "glue sniffer"', British Medical Journal, 2, 29-30.

26. Russ, G., Clarkson, A.R., Woodruff, A.J., Seymour, A.E. and Cheng, I.K.P. (1981), 'Renal failure from "glue sniffing"', Medical Journal of Australia, 2, 121-2.

27. Fischman, C.M. and Oster, J.R. (1979), 'Toxic effects of toluene', Journal of the American Medical Association, 241(16), 1713-15.

28. Kroeger, R.M., Moore, R.J., Lehman, T.H., Giesy, J.D. and Skeeters, C.E. (1981), 'Recurrent urinary calculi associated with toluene sniffing', Journal of Urology, 123, 89-91.

29. Voigts, A. and Kaufman, C.E. (1983), 'Acidosis and other metabolic abnormalities associated with paint sniffing', Southern Medical Journal, 76(4), 443-7, 452.

30. Rawlins, M.D. and Davies, D.M. (1984), 'Adverse drug reactions', Medicine International, 2, 290-4.

31. Valpey, R., Sumi, S.M., Copass, M.K. and Goble, G.J. (1978), 'Acute and chronic progressive encephalopathy due to gasoline sniffing', Neurology, 28(5), 507-10.
32. Young, R.S.K., Grzyb, S.E. and Crismon, L. (1977), 'Recurrent cerebellar dysfunction as related to chronic gasoline sniffing in an adolescent girl', Clinical Paediatrics, 16(8), 706-8.
33. Seshia, S.S., Rajani, K.R., Boeckx, R.L. and Chow, P.N. (1978), 'The neurological manifestations of chronic inhalation of leaded gasoline', Developmental Medicine and Child Neurology, 20, 323-34.
34. Yamamura, Y. (1969), 'n-hexane polyneuropathy', Folia Psychiatrica et Neurologica Japonica, 23(1), 45-57.
35. Towfighi, J., Gonatas, N.K., Pleasure, D., Cooper, H.S. and McCree, L. 'Glue sniffer's neuropathy', Neurology, 26, 238-43.
36. Korobkin, R., Asbury, A.K., Sumner, A.J. and Nielsen, S.L. (1975), 'Glue-sniffing neuropathy', Arch. Neurol, 32, 158-62.
37. Satran, R. and Dodson, V.N. (1963), 'Toluene habituation: report of a case', New England Journal of Medicine, 268(13), 719-21.
38. Grabski, D.A. (1961), 'Toluene sniffing producing cerebellar degeneration', American Journal of Psychiatry, 118, 461-2.
39. Knox, J.W. and Nelson, J.R. (1966), 'Permanent encephalopathy from toluene inhalation', New England Journal of Medicine, 275, 1494-6.
40. Malm, G. and Lying-Tunell, U. (1980), 'Cerebellar dysfunction related to toluene sniffing', Acta Neurol. Scandinav., 62, 191-2.
41. Sasa, M., Igarashi, S., Miyazaki, K., Nakano, S. and Matsuoka, I. (1978), 'Equilibrium disorders with diffuse brain atrophy in long term toluene sniffing', Archives of Oto-Rhino-Laryngology, 221, 163-9.
42. Lewis, J.D., Moritz, D. and Mellis, L.P. (1981), 'Long term toluene abuse', American Journal of Psychiatry, 138(3), 368-70.
43. Ehyai, A. and Freeman, F.R. (1983), 'Progressive optic neuropathy and sensorineural hearing loss due to chronic glue sniffing', Journal of Neurology, Neurosurgery and Psychiatry, 46, 349-51.

44. Schikler, K.N. Seitz, K., Rice, J.F. and Strader, T. (1982), 'Solvent abuse associated cortical atrophy', Journal of Adolescent Health Care, 3, 37-9.
45. Watson, J.M. (1980), 'Solvent Abuse', Medicine Science and Law, 20(2), 137.
46. Will, A.M. and McLaren, E.H. (1981), 'Reversible renal damage due to glue sniffing', British Medical Journal, 283(6290), 525-6.
47. Allister, C., Lush, M., Oliver, J.S. and Watson, J.M. (1981), 'Status epilepticus caused by solvent abuse', British Medical Journal, 283(6300), 1156.
48. Lamont, C.M. and Adams, F.G. (1982), 'Glue-sniffing as a cause of a positive radio-isotope brain scan', European Journal of Nuclear Medicine, 7, 387-8.
49. Alha, A., Korte, T. and Tenhu, M. (1973), 'Solvent sniffing deaths', Rechtsmedizin, 72(4), 299-305.
50. Kringsholm, B. (1980), 'Sniffing-associated deaths in Denmark', Forensic Science International, 15, 215-25.
51. Watson, J.M. (1979), 'Morbidity and mortality statistics on solvent abuse', Medicine, Science and Law, 19(4), 246-52.
52. Anderson, H.R., Macnair, R.S. and Ramsey, J.D. (1985), 'Deaths from volatile substance abuse: a national epidemiological study', British Medical Journal, 290(6464), 304-7.

Chapter Seven

SOLVENT ABUSE IN THE FAMILY

One factor strikingly absent from the literature is any mention of discussions with parents of solvent abusers about their children and the associated problems. Parents have been mentioned frequently in the American literature on solvent abuse and have often been described as unloving, alcoholic and hostile to their children. In an extensive search of the world literature, the author was unable to find any comments from parents about solvent abuse or any mention of structured interviews with them.

Since 1975, the author has seen the parents of 788 individuals who were referred on account of solvent abuse. They were seen in a variety of different settings such as health centres, police stations, clinics and sometimes in their own homes. Usually they were interviewed by the author on one or two occasions when they accompanied their children who were attending for a check on their physical health. In the case of the 101 habitual sniffers already mentioned in earlier chapters, some parents were seen several times over a period of weeks or months. Information from parents was collected but the interviews were informal and unstructured although some were recorded on tape with the consent of the parents. While the information obtained was descriptive rather than analytical and the limitations of such information are obvious, it is interesting and provides valuable insight into parental attitudes to solvent abuse which should not be ignored.

Some parents of habitual sniffers described problems that had been present before the onset of the solvent abuse but others said that the problems only started at the same time as the solvent abuse. The parents, without exception, were found to be puzzled and sometimes angry about the fact that

their children abused solvents. None could
understand why their children were involved in this
activity and some expressed the view that they
would have preferred their children to have become
involved in drinking alcohol rather than sniffing
substances as a means of intoxication because at
least they felt that they could understand that and
in some cases could have accepted it.


## Health

Regardless of the extent of the child's involvement
in solvent abuse, all parents were extremely
worried about their child's health and wanted
reassurance that no harm had been done. They were
sometimes so concerned that they would travel many
miles to get advice. This was particularly
noticeable in the case of the parents of children
with some previous health problems such as asthma
or convulsions.

The parents whose children had been habitually
involved in solvent abuse over long periods of time
all expressed deep concern about possible long-term
damage to liver, kidneys and brain. All seemed
grateful for the opportunity to talk about solvent
abuse and its impact on their children and all were
very reassured by the information that physical
damage did not seem to occur often, if at all. They
said that what they found even more reassuring was
the medical examination of their children and the
blood tests to check for liver and kidney damage
which might not show up in the clinical examination.
Only a very small number of parents specifically
mentioned fears that their children might become
addicted to solvents and none mentioned fears that
the abuse of other substances such as alcohol might
follow.


## Behaviour

In general, parents were mainly concerned with
health matters in relation to solvent abuse.
However, the parents of the 101 habitual sniffers
expressed a great deal of anxiety about the conduct
of their children and described five main kinds of
problem. The first of these came from the
difficulties of coping in the family home with
episodes of acute intoxication caused by the
solvent abuse. The next was the need to deal with

Solvent Abuse in the Family

the mess and smell caused by the substances and
bags used in the practice and which were sometimes
kept in large quantities in the house by their
child. The third was the deterioration of the
individual with regard to personal hygiene and
relationships in the home and displays of
unprovoked, aggressive behaviour between episodes
of acute intoxication. Fourthly came the difficulties
of coping with the results of anti-social behaviour
which occurred outside the home. Finally the
parents had endured constant anxieties about the
current situation as well as fears about the future
and many expressed doubts about whether their
children would ever mature sufficiently to give up
the habit.


## Acute Intoxication

The difficulties of coping with intoxicated
individuals were mentioned by some of the 101 sets
of parents. The problem that upset most of them was
that they could not trust the children sufficiently
to leave them in the house because they realised
that before they came back they were likely to have
been indulging in solvent abuse. When the children
were in this acutely intoxicated state, it was
impossible to conduct any kind of dialogue with
them and some parents specifically mentioned that
violence was shown to them and to brothers and
sisters. Some parents mentioned the sense of
helplessness when their children came home not just
intoxicated but also with clothes which were
covered with glue and often torn.


## The Impedimenta of Glue Sniffing

Most of the parents of the social sniffers made no
comments on any practical domestic difficulties
associated with their children's practice. However
the parents of the habitual sniffers all commented
on the difficulties of removing various substances,
mainly glue, from their children's clothes. Some
bought other solvents to remove the sticky stains
and others found that they had to replace the
clothes. A few parents described other problems.
For example, eight parents described the large cans
of adhesive and discarded bags which might be found
on the tops of wardrobes, under beds or mattresses
from sniffing sessions that took place in the home.

Solvent Abuse in the Family

One mother discovered 200 glue-filled bags while tidying her son's room one day. Another had found large numbers of bags and cans hidden in a cupboard and a third had come across them in the cistern of the toilet. A further four parents mentioned substances and bags lying about the house. These mothers all complained bitterly about the overwhelming smell of solvents in the house and also about the mess involved. All had been obliged to buy solvent-based cleaning materials to remove the stains which further added to the smell. Some mothers were also worried about the fire risk due to all these inflammable substances being in the home.


## Family Relationships

The 101 habitual sniffers were all males, aged 13 to 15, who were described as having previously enjoyed a very close relationship with their mothers. The parents explained how their children's problems with family relationships increased as they became more involved in solvent abuse. The abusers never took a share of any chores about the house and their behaviour became increasingly difficult and aggressive to the point where they were said to assault siblings and kick them without provocation. As a result, previously good relation-ships with siblings deteriorated. On occasions, the parents and sometimes the other children in the family might have to spend all night looking for the habitual sniffers who had failed to return home. Because of these problems in the family, life became stressful and tempers were frayed.

The personal cleanliness of the sniffers tended to suffer as time went on since they would not take baths or wear clean clothes without a great deal of fuss. Because of the wear and tear on clothing caused by the intoxication and aggressive behaviour, and the glue itself, their clothes, shoes and books required to be replaced more often than those of their brothers or sisters. In addition, the mothers said that they found themselves neglecting other members of the family because of the time, ,money and effort required to cope with the trouble caused by a son who habitually sniffed solvents.

There were two other serious family problems expressed by these parents about their sons. One

concerned the thefts from the parental home. At
first, the stealing was confined to money but it
later involved any object which could be sold or
pawned. Two mothers described how they had to keep
special objects or clothes at their sisters' homes
to protect them from theft. Several mothers
described vividly how upset they had felt when they
had to explain to their other children about a
prized stamp or coin collection, a special uniform
or a Christmas gift from an aunt or godmother which
had gone missing and which was later discovered to
have been sold by their brother to raise money to
maintain his solvent abuse. The other anxiety which
recurred for these mothers was that the younger
children would also turn to solvent abuse as they
grew up and started to imitate their older brother.
They were not aware of this having happened on any
occasion but these mothers knew that their sons had
started off on solvent abuse by copying others and
they feared that the same thing might happen to
their other, younger children.


## Behaviour Outside the Home

Most solvent abusers seemed to have indulged the
habit outside their homes so that their mothers did
not experience the problems and difficulties that
have just been described. However, almost half of
the parents of habitual users and some of the other
mothers described problems associated with various
kinds of deviant behaviour in the community. The
police sometimes brought their child home because
he or she had been found intoxicated on solvents or
because of their aggressive and violent behaviour.
Sometimes theft was involved and occasionally there
was more serious anti-social behaviour such as
assault. In the case of younger children, the
police sometimes searched the district for them
because they had been reported as missing from
home. Many parents found that this was entirely
unsatisfactory but did not know what to do about
it. A few kept their children at home by confining
them to their rooms and some even boarded up the
windows but inevitably the children escaped.
Sometimes they even went out in the nude if their
parents had removed their clothes in the hope that
this would keep them in. All the mothers and
fathers expressed anxiety, resignation or sometimes
anger about all these events which occurred not
infrequently with glue sniffing children.

Solvent Abuse in the Family

## Relationships Outside the Family

When the parents described the relationships which
their children had formed outside the home, many of
them said that their children had befriended
different types of people after starting solvent
abuse and that they no longer had any knowledge of
their child's friends. Some parents viewed these
relationships with suspicion because they felt that
the new friends were a bad influence on their
child. In general, mothers felt that everything
that was best in the family was being undermined.
The parents of those who had always been lone
sniffers or who had gradually become more involved
on their own expressed anxieties about their
child's increasing isolation from other people.

## Education

Only the parents of habitual sniffers had worries
about their child's education and most commented
that their child had missed a great deal of
education but this was really overshadowed by other
problems. Generally, these children truanted more
and more until they became more isolated in school
and finally dropped out. The parents did not seem
to be particularly anxious about missed education
although it represented part of the general anxiety
and dissatisfaction which they expressed.

## Children in Residential Establishments

Parents were not the only people to complain about
the behaviour of solvent abusers. A survey of the
social work residential establishments in Strathclyde
showed that the staff there had also found that
solvent abusers presented problems of behaviour
such as theft, vandalism, and persistent disruption.
Solvent abuse taking place in the homes and other
problems at school were also mentioned. These
problems were described by care workers in
children's homes, assessment centres and List D
schools and this confirmed that the children still
behaved in the same way even after they were
removed from their own homes into residential care.

Solvent Abuse in the Family

## The Future

Most parents of the habitual sniffers were extremely worried about what the future held for their children. Many had gone through long periods of hoping that things would improve and of taking their children to one agency or another for help and guidance. However, as time passed, most began to realise that the whole family would need to be involved and not just the solvent abuser alone and many became aware that the solvent abuser did not think that he needed any help. Eventually they became resigned to the fact that the problem was likely to continue.

Several mothers were afraid that these children, whom they had always considered to be immature and unable to accept responsibility, even prior to their solvent abuse, would continue like that as they became adults. There is every indication that this was so in some cases but others made remarkable progress once they had matured and particularly after they had acquired their own flats and moved away from their families.

## Case 1

Parents discovered that their 14 year-old-child had been introduced to glue sniffing at the local community centre. As a result, they were upset and concerned and had a discussion with their son about the matter. Until then, they had heard very little about the practice but knew that it was mainly an adolescent prank. After a few months, they were shocked to find out that he was involved in glue sniffing almost every day. He used to gaze vacantly into space at home and at school he started to fall behind in his work because he had no physical energy and no interest in his studies. Because of this, his parents contacted a psychologist for help but the boy continued to deteriorate. He lost a lot of weight so that his bones began to stick out. He continued to sit and stare into space, he repeatedly absconded from school and on occasions went missing from home for up to two days at a time. His parents began to take it in turns to look after him at home. They also took it in turns to take him to his teacher but by the morning interval he would have gone. The police helped a great deal by searching for the boy and returning him to his parents and sometimes the parents themselves found

161

him by searching the district. The boy frequently
lost his clothes or his belongings and sometimes
had accidents although these were seldom serious.
On occasions he would sell his personal belongings
to raise money to buy glue

Like many other parents in a similar
situation, the parents sought professional help to
deal with the problem. At first, they took their
son to a doctor who said that, in his opinion, it
was a passing phase. They then took him to a
psychiatrist who suggested that the boy might be
given more personal freedom. However, as time
passed and the behaviour continued to deteriorate,
they took him to another doctor and an appointment
was made for them to see someone from the social
work department. By this time the boy was truanting
two or three times per week and, in spite of their
reservations, the parents thought that it would be
helpful if they could have him admitted to an
assessment centre. It was not possible at that time
but the boy later committed a breach of the peace
while intoxicated and as a result was brought
before the Children's Panel. One of the panel
members agreed with the parents that the boy should
be admitted to an assessment centre and this duly
happened.

The parents worried constantly about their son
and visited him three times weekly. He broke out of
the centre and went missing several times. On one
of these occasions, he broke his wrist in a fall
from the roof of a building. After this, he
gradually began to improve in appearance and
behaviour and soon was allowed out, once a week at
first and then for weekends. He finally went home
just after his 15th birthday. He readjusted well to
school but left when he was 16 without sitting his
'O Grade' examinations. Subsequently, this boy did
very well. His appearance is neat and he now has a
good job. He has passed his driving test and
acquired his own flat. He has a steady girlfriend
and sees his parents regularly.

This boy's mother is of the opinion that
solvent abuse and the associated behaviour should
be treated early rather than late.

Case 2

The parents of a 13-year-old boy became puzzled and
alarmed by his changed behaviour. He had always
been a fairly biddable child and one who, while

Solvent Abuse in the Family

immature, was always popular with his friends. He
began to stay out late and even to disappear for
hours at a time. It was also noticed that none of
his friends came to the house any more. He
occasionally stayed out at night until he was
brought home by the police. His parents did not
know what all this meant. They knew about the glue
sniffing which was common in the district and they
also knew about the tell-tale signs of glue on the
face, hands and clothes of people indulging in it.
They had read about the spots that sometimes
occurred on the faces of sniffers. Their child
showed none of these signs and they were convinced
that their son was not sniffing glue.

One day, a friend told them that their boy had
been sniffing glue a few times and it turned out
that several other people also knew of this but had
not liked to say anything. They confronted the boy
with this information but he denied it and
continued to deny it although his behaviour quite
obviously was continuing to deteriorate. He began
to come home noticeably high on glue or,
alternatively, he failed to return at all until
eventually brought home by the police. More denials
followed and, even after money disappeared from the
home, there were still more denials. At no time did
any solvent abuse take place at home.

A puppy arrived in the house which he
desperately wanted for himself. When he came home
one day to find that his sister had taken it for a
walk, he became violent, almost threw her down the
stairs and, when his mother intervened, he hit her.
At this point, his mother telephoned the police to
say that she considered her son to be beyond her
control and she wanted him taken away from home.
The police arranged for the boy to be referred to
the Reporter as a matter of urgency. The boy and
his parents went to the Children's Panel and he was
admitted to an assessment centre where he remained
for several months. During that time, the boy built
up a very good relationship with his social
workers, was visited regularly by his parents and
was even allowed home at weekends.

He came home for a short period before leaving
school at 16. He is now 18, is doing well, lives in
his own flat and has a regular girlfriend. He
visits his parents quite regularly and sometimes
stays with them without causing any problems. His
mother says that he was always an immature child
who could not accept responsibility but she now
feels that he is maturing rapidly and that his

163

attitude to life has changed considerably.

His parents have remarked that on numerous occasions they felt ostracised because their son was known to be a glue sniffer. The other children in the family have also felt that they were regarded very cautiously at school because of their brother's involvement. The relationships at home suffered very much because of what happened but are now considered by all the family to be greatly improved.


Conclusions

Parental worries and difficulties have received no attention in the literature but it should now be clear that consideration of these factors must play an important part in the management of any case of glue sniffing. All parents who were seen expressed grave concern about the possible health hazards of solvent abuse and needed reassurance that their children had not suffered any permanent damage. They were greatly encouraged when their children were given a medical examination and no abnormalities were discovered. When they were told that solvent abuse was usually a passing phase of short duration, they were very relieved.

The parents of the habitual abusers were very anxious, not only about the possible health implications, but also about the related behaviour problems and their impact on family and social relationships. These parents were unable to relax in view of the multiple difficulties that their children's behaviour was causing. When parents of different sniffers met it was amazing to see how well and how quickly they were able to feel an affinity for one another in spite of being strangers from different backgrounds and coming from various parts of Strathclyde. They were soon sharing their problems, experiences and anxieties. Sometimes parents could be put in touch with one another by the author to their mutual benefit although quite often this was not possible.

Some of these parents said that the police had been very helpful but that otherwise they had encountered great difficulty in obtaining help and guidance for their children or for themselves. Sometimes they were simply told that glue sniffing was just a passing phase and that they should not be excessively concerned about it. Later, when it had become clear that the solvent abuse represented

more than a passing phase, they were still unable
to find what they considered to be appropriate
help. Most said that they had approached all the
available agencies without being offered any
practical assistance. Without exception they felt
that the underlying problem could not be tackled
until the solvent abuse had stopped. The apparent
impossibility of achieving this was very disccuraging
and the whole affair seemed to them to be a vicious
circle.

Clearly, it is all very well to be reassuring
and to say to the majority of parents that solvent
abuse is just a passing phase but for some young
people it is a long and difficult part of their
lives which presents their parents with a very
trying experience. Many of the parents are
certainly not the alcoholic, unloving and uncaring
people described in the literature on solvent abuse
and their need for help is very real.

Chapter Eight

THE RESPONSE IN STRATHCLYDE

Solvent abuse was identified relatively recently in Britain compared to its first appearance in America and Canada. Researchers in these countries had already described several forms of solvent abuse. In particular, it was suggested that emotional difficulties could lead to chronic solvent abuse as a form of escape from unpleasant situations which caused a lack of security or a loss of self-esteem.[1,2] The solvent abuse in such cases could not be seen as an isolated entity but as a symptom of underlying difficulties. Medical, psychotherapeutic and residential treatments were all mentioned as being suitable for chronic solvent abusers. 'Quiet deterioration' has been said to be an appropriate term to apply to the condition of the habitual sniffer.[3] Those who indulged in habitual solvent abuse have been described as becoming very thin, suffering from emotional problems and withdrawing from social contacts. Individual or group therapy, occupational therapy, probation, foster homes and training schools were all found to be unsuccessful.[2] The most promising approach was said to be a multiple one involving the individual, his peer group and his family. The school situation was also said to require assessment since it was likely that failure at school and subsequent truancy featured in the life of the habitual sniffer. However, in spite of all this effort at rehabilitation, the treatment of the chronic abuser of solvents was described as being very difficult.

This then is the background of information from other countries which might prove useful in dealing with solvent abuse in this country. This chapter describes some responses and strategies which were tried in Strathclyde.

The Response in Strathclyde

## Multi-disciplinary Groups

Solvent abuse in what is now the Lanark division of Strathclyde was first identified by the police who responded to the problem by drawing it to the attention of social workers, health care professionals and teachers. A multidisciplinary working party on solvent abuse was set up in January 1976 to collate the available information on the subject and to promote co-ordination between the professional groups concerned.

From mid-1976, Solvent Abuse Committees were set up in some districts of the Glasgow division of Strathclyde. These were formed by professional people such as general practitioners, psychiatrists, community doctors and nurses, teachers, police, social workers and health educators and they met regularly at a local level. The purpose was to exchange relevant information about solvent abuse and to discuss any problems occurring locally with a view to developing suitable strategies. Important discussions took place about the role of each professional group in relation to solvent abuse. In these early days practical advice at a personal level could be obtained from other members of the committee and referrals to various agencies could be arranged. One vital factor was that each person had an opportunity to view solvent abuse from perspectives other than his or her own or that of their particular discipline.

In one district, the Clinical Co-ordinator of Child Health Services maintained a list of solvent abusers. The names of all young people found under the influence of solvents on three occasions were notified on a confidential basis by the agency who discovered them and then recorded on the list. When the same name appeared frequently, it was possible for the co-ordinator to refer the child to a psychiatrist. This system was abandoned when it became clear that once a name was notified and entered in the register it stayed there permanently. There was no mechanism for reviewing the names and the list became longer as time passed until the scheme was discontinued.

In another district, discovery of a solvent abuser might lead to a home visit by a specialised team drawn from the School Health Service. This group was responsible for assessing not only the child and his solvent abuse but also his home circumstances. Referral to a psychiatrist was one of the possibilities in the follow-up programme.

## Emergency Treatment

The treatment required in emergency cases of solvent abuse was never in doubt. Cases of acute intoxication, accidents or other adverse events were treated by the police, medical and nursing staffs in the same way as any other incidents of a similar nature. Initially, there was a demand for detailed information about specific points relating to solvent intoxication but this decreased after a few cases had been successfully treated. Sometimes, details about first-aid treatment were requested by people such as teachers or youth workers so that they could cope with any individual who might have become unconscious. Information of this kind was discussed at local meetings of the Solvent Abuse Committees. The treatment of these acute situations was straightforward but this was not so in the management of individual cases of solvent abuse. In spite of the Solvent Abuse Committees or other groups, there was a lack of co-ordination in the management of individual cases and the methods used were often haphazard and dependent on the particular professional group dealing with the matter.

## The Medical/Police Clinic

In October 1978, a clinic was set up by the author in a police station in the east end of Glasgow in collaboration with the police. Originally it was funded by a grant from the British Medical Association with the aim of providing information about solvent abuse in the district (see Chapter 5) and also of determining if any harm was sustained by those who indulged in the practice. After consultation with the police, the sessions of the clinic were held once a week between 6 and 9 p.m. Personnel from the Community Involvement Branch were also involved in the project.

Children aged 16 or younger could be referred to the clinic by any professional person or by parents and all referrals were encouraged. Attendance was entirely voluntary and children were seen only if accompanied by a parent or guardian. When the children arrived at the clinic, they and their parents would be met by someone from the police Community Involvement Branch. He or she carried out an initial interview to assess the situation and offer counselling and advice on the risks of solvent abuse to the child and parents. They were then taken to the police surgeon's office to be interviewed by the doctor about solvent abuse and any other family problems. A medical examination followed and this included the taking of a blood sample to detect any dysfunction of liver or kidneys.

The clinic provided a good opportunity to offer health education and counselling to children and parents. Children were usually seen once only. Parents and family doctors were notified within a week about the results of the blood tests. There was no actual follow-up of cases but the clinic offered an open-door policy and parents were encouraged to return if there were any further problems. Only 16 per cent of the 134 children seen in the first year were seen again because of repeated solvent abuse. This suggests that the clinic had a useful effect in curbing the extent of solvent abuse in the area. The clinic was intended to be a screening clinic only and was not designed to offer long term management of cases of solvent abuse. Children with problems were referred from the clinic to appropriate agencies such as social work departments or psychiatric clinics.

After the experimental period of the first year, it was decided to retain the clinic and it is still in operation in 1985. It is staffed by Community Involvement personnel and psychiatrists. This has made possible the collection of more detailed information on psychiatric as well as physical dysfunction in solvent abuse. According to a recent publication, the incidence of psychiatric disorders in 300 children seen at the clinic was found to be very low. However, the psychiatrists involved considered it very important that a full assessment should be carried out by a trained person in every case in order to find out whether or not psychiatric referral was required.[4] In addition to this assessment, the children could, with parental consent, be placed under the supervision of a plain-clothes Community Involvement officer for up to eight weeks. During this time, the police could offer advice and support to the parents while arranging for the young person to be involved in swimming, boxing, football, youth clubs and other diversionary activities.

During the second year of the clinc, the number of referrals increased to 169. Children were told that their friends were welcome to attend the clinic. Only 19 per cent of those seen returned for a second visit and 6.7 per cent for a third. The clinic now offers a range of services for children and parents and further referral to other agencies is easily achieved.

## The Medical Psychotherapy Centre

Another centre dealing with solvent abuse was set up in the East End of Glasgow in September 1980 based at a day hospital. Its aims were to provide an assessment of solvent abuse, to establish management programmes for individual cases when required and to provide in-service training for medical or nursing staff and social workers as well as any other interested professionals. This multi-disciplinary team is headed by a psychiatrist and includes one general practitioner, three nursing staff, one social worker, two occupational therapists, a teacher and a clinical psychologist. Originally, the clinic was held on Saturday mornings but increased demand had led to additional sessions on Wednesday evenings.

Table 8.1: Treatment Programmes for Solvent Abusers at a Glasgow Day Hospital

| | |
|---|---|
| 1. | Individual psychotherapy |
| 2. | Group therapy |
| 3. | Art therapy |
| 4. | Social skills |
| 5. | Relaxation therapy |
| 6. | Hypnotherapy |
| 7. | Occupational and diversional therapy |
| 8. | Counselling of parents |
| 9. | Help with reading and writing (by qualified literary tutors) |

Every effort is made to encourage the friends of sniffers to come to the clinic and parental attendance is actively sought. This clinic offers a range of treatments for those attending, any of whom may be referred by a professional group or parents. Self-referrals are also accepted and the management is determined according to individual needs. The programme involves an initial interview with the doctor or nursing staff followed by assessments of the individual, the family and the home situation. General physical and neurological examinations are carried out and blood samples taken for tests. Further examinations are then carried out by a psychiatrist, psychologist or social worker. After the first appointment, the individual is seen regularly by the staff. A range of treatment programmes is available as shown in Table 8.1.

## The Psychology/Social Work Clinic

In one district a different method was used and this involved a group approach to chronic glue sniffers. A clinic staffed by social workers and psychologists was set up. Referrals were accepted from the police, schools, social workers and parents and there were occasional self-referrals. To ensure that the individuals who attended were involved habitually, two or more of the following requirements had to be met.

1. Sniffing for longer than six months.
2. Missing school or work due to glue sniffing.
3. Sniffing currently more than four times per week.
4. Sniffing alone as well as with a group.
5. Finding it hard to give up the habit without help or support.

The most common reason given by the adolescents for wanting to come to the clinic was that they feared the dangers but at the same time they felt that solvent abuse had taken control of their lives.
For three months after the start of the programme, the chronic sniffers met as a group. A behavioural approach was used in which the sniffers kept diaries recording the amount of glue taken, when it was taken and the reasons for indulging. Reasonable targets were set for each week with a view to cutting down the quantity of glue used or the frequency of sessions. This approach had to be modified when it was learned that those group members who were finding it most difficult to give up the habit were actively encouraging the others to sniff more. They exchanged information about

easy access to glue and were mocking those who were managing to achieve their aims. A positive reinforcement towards sniffing developed in the group in spite of the workers' efforts to achieve the opposite.

At that stage, the management programme was changed and the therapists began to see the children on an individual basis but, occasionally, they would see them in pairs if the two of them always sniffed together. A counselling approach was not introduced although diaries and targets could still be used in specific cases if they were thought to be helpful. The current practice is to work with each sniffer individually following an initial interview with the parents to explain what these sessions aim to achieve. Children can attend weekly or fortnightly depending on how difficult it is for the individual to cut down and finally stop the abuse of solvents.


Intermediate Treatment Projects

Some interesting projects have been undertaken by Intermediate Treatment (IT) workers. In one district, a senior IT worker turned his attention to solvent abuse working on the theory that those who were indulging would provide support for one another in a concerted effort to stop the habit. He planned an approach similar to that used by Alcoholics Anonymous with modifications suitable for youngsters involved in solvent abuse. However, in practice he found that the group approach encouraged continuation of the habit rather than abstinence from it.

Another group was formed which mixed glue sniffers with other children who had different problems. This seemed to work with casual sniffers but not with chronic sniffers who were said to need more individual help. The IT worker concerned would like to see the establishment of a refuge for chronic sniffers where they could be seen and counselled in a neutral environment which was neither part of the List D school nor of the hospital system.

In another part of Glasgow, an IT unit tried a different management approach in which glue sniffers were integrated into existing groups of children. Group help and support were emphasised as being more important than individual counselling. The chronic abusers were referred to more

specialised services such as family therapy or
adolescent units. One very interesting aspect of
the strategy was that it used the help of recovered
solvent abusers to influence the peer group abusers
by providing them with a framework of experience.
Another IT project involved the setting up of
a street solvent abuse group to work in the streets
of a local community in order to study the extent
of solvent abuse and to find out the needs of those
involved in the practice with a view to social work
or IT intervention. On assessing the situation, the
IT workers found that it was serious since a number
of youngsters, aged 10 to 16, were involved in the
dangerous practices of sniffing aerosols and butane
as well as glue sniffing. After this discovery, the
IT workers changed their immediate aim to that of
reducing the potential dangers of the practice
before attempting to achieve longer-term goals.
First, they taught basic first-aid to the young
people and then discussed with them the fact that
the sniffing of some substances, such as cleaning
fluids, was more harmful than inhaling glues. They
also stressed that the abuse of butane and aerosols
could be very dangerous, depending on the methods
used. They provided a contact point for the young
people and guaranteed confidentiality to anyone who
wanted to talk about personal difficulties. IT
workers were available for this service every day
between 1 and 5 p.m. An open group meeting was also
held weekly with tea and biscuits, drawing
materials and games provided. An evening meeting
was planned in order to inform local adults about
the dangers and problems of solvent abuse with the
additional objective of encouraging children and
parents to talk together as a first step towards
breaking down the barriers to communication.
The outcome of this work was interesting. The
use of aerosol sprays and butane stopped very
quickly. Within a month, children had started to
drop in to talk about their personal and family
problems and, within another two months, the
solvent abuse had stopped altogether. The evening
meeting was a great success. Representatives from
the police, Social Work Department and Reporter's
office attended along with 45 young people. Not one
parent came. Following this meeting, a 'girls only'
open group was formed at the request of the
children and consisted of twelve girls aged 10 to
15 years. After this group had been set up, only
one girl subsequently abused solvents during a
three-month period and this happened on one

occasion only. It was hoped to make arrangements
for one or two day trips for the children and there
was also the possibility of a residential holiday
for a few of the most vulnerable.


Social Work Projects

In one district, in response to a high incidence of
solvent abuse, an information point and meeting
place for parents and their children was set up by
social workers in a community flat. Despite wide
advertising, the use made of the facility was very
poor. The reason suggested by the social workers
for the poor response was the location of the
meeting place which made anonymity impossible.
    Another social work team project was set up to
combat solvent abuse in a district which had very
poor leisure facilities. The social workers met
groups of parents who were interested in knowing
more about solvent abuse and in contributing some
resources. This group, which met fortnightly,
invited doctors, police and social workers to come
and give them information about solvent abuse which
could then be passed on to other parents who had
encountered the practice. The parents and social
workers subsequently investigated the possibility
of starting a city farm as a means of combating the
lack of leisure activities. The social workers saw
this as a useful and positive way of bringing
together children and adults in a community
project.


Schools

Attempts were made in Strathclyde schools to
identify children who were heavily involved in glue
sniffing. In doing so, it was planned to have them
medically examined, monitor their educational
progress and to refer them for help to a child
guidance clinic or educational psychologist.
Teachers in these schools described the marked
changes of temperament and personality of those
children who were habitually involved and remarked
on the disruptive influence they exerted on the
other children at school. Another feature noted was
that children who habitually abused solvents fell
behind with their school work and subsequently
truanted. Some teachers were of the opinion that a
whole range of activities would have to be created

for these children and that modifications to their
school curriculum were also required.


Residential Establishments

In May 1982, a survey was carried out in
Strathclyde residential establishments for children
including children's homes, intermediate training
centres, List D schools and assessment centres. In
this way, 163 children who abused solvents were
identified. Various strategies were employed by
staff to enable them to cope with these solvent
abusers. Individual counselling was used most
frequently except in the intermediate training
centre where the strategies most commonly employed
were diversionary leisure activities, group work
involving abusers and non-abusers and education of
the children about the risks of solvent abuse. Over
all, the methods of management used were individual
counselling (86 per cent) the use of leisure
activities (80 per cent), banning solvent abuse on
the premises (62 per cent), education about the
risks (76 per cent) and regularly involving the
child's social worker in management (65 per cent).
Six indicators were used to test the effectiveness
of the management and these are shown in Table 8.2.
They relate to the abuse of solvents per se,
general behaviour, the adoption of more positive
interests and the forming of relationships with
other children, staff and parents. Overall, the
intervention was found to be successful as shown on
Table 8.3.


Table 8.2: Strathclyde Social Work Residential Establishments
- Indicators of Success in Management of Solvent Abuse


| 1. | Use of solvents | (a) | Stopped completely |
| | | (b) | Stopped except at weekends |
| | | (c) | Not altered |
| | | (d) | Not known |
| 2. | General behaviour | (a) | Improved |
| | | (b) | Remained the same |
| | | (c) | Deteriorated |
| | | (d) | Not known |

Table 8.2 (Cont'd)

---

| | | | |
|---|---|---|---|
| 3. | Interests switched to more positive activities | (a)<br>(b) | Yes<br>Not known |
| 4. | Relationships with other children | (a)<br>(b)<br>(c)<br>(d) | Improved<br>Remained the same<br>Deteriorated<br>Not known |
| 5. | Relationships with staff | (a)<br>(b)<br>(c)<br>(d) | Improved<br>Remained the same<br>Deteriorated<br>Not known |
| 6. | Relationships with parents | (a)<br>(b)<br>(c)<br>(d) | Improved<br>Remained the same<br>Deteriorated<br>Not known |

---

Table 8.3: Strathclyde Social Work Residential Establishments - Results of Intervention in Solvent Abuse

---

| | | |
|---|---|---|
| 1. | Solvent abuse | 40% stopped<br>13% stopped except at weekends |
| 2. | General behaviour | 51% improved |
| 3. | Change to more positive activities | 49% had done so |
| 4. | Relationships with other children | 35% showed improvement |
| 5. | Relationships with staff | 59% showed improvement |
| 6. | Relationships with parents | 37% showed improvement |

---

The areas in which the staff were presented with the greatest difficulties were lack of basic knowledge about solvent abuse, insufficient facilities for chronic sniffers, inadequate funding and lack of facilities for diversionary activities. Links between the area team from the Social Work Department and the health services were also thought to be inadequate.

Parent Groups

Parent self-help groups were set up in some districts with the help of local Social Work Departments. The purpose of these was to provide parents with a way of helping and supporting each other and also to increase their knowledge about solvent abuse and its implications. Some of these groups have been reported to be particularly active.

Health Education in Schools

All of the projects and strategies mentioned so far have related to dealing with people who were involved in solvent abuse - directly as abusers or indirectly, for example as parents. At the same time, a health education approach has been developing in schools in order to prevent children starting solvent abuse. Initially, the amount of information about solvent abuse given was left to the discretion of individual head teachers. However, in 1980, a decision was taken by the Education Committee of Strathclyde Regional Council that schools must make some contribution towards the prevention of problems arising from solvent abuse. The schools were seen as being in a position to act positively along with other agencies and parents since they shared responsibilities for the well-being of the young people.

The group working on this classroom initiative considered that the schools might play two significant roles in primary prevention: (1) by stopping initial experimentation with solvent abuse and (2) by reducing harmful effects if experimentation did take place. Teaching material was to be prepared giving a clear statement about solvent abuse and was to be presented in a way that stimulated young people to think about the situation and to develop a responsible attitude towards themselves and other people. The standard of language used throughout was designed to be suitable for pupils in the first and second years of secondary school although it was considered possible to use it with younger or older children if necessary. It was thought desirable to ensure that education on solvent abuse be introduced at an appropriately early stage if the attitudes of young people were to be influenced away from involvement. The educational material was produced in both audio and audio-visual form, with work-card exercises, and material suitable for class and group work. It was envisaged that individual schools would use, adapt or extend it according to their particular needs.

It was hoped that schools in areas where solvent abuse was a problem would make use of these educational packages and it was suggested that an effective setting for this would be within a co-ordinated social education programme that included health education. Various aspects of staff training, the use of the material and extent of parental consultation have all been considered. The programme became available in January 1983 and has been used in 20 schools as a pilot scheme where it was well received by the teaching staff. It is now available to all schools in Strathclyde.

Other material is currently being prepared by the Department of Education on decision-making and other life skills which will be available in video-cassette form. It is generally recognised that the schools can make a valuable contribution towards education for healthy living and also to the establishment of responsible attitudes among young people. This approach is clearly aimed at solving underlying problems and is an endeavour to influence the decision making process in children that leads to solvent abuse as distinct from dealing with the practice of solvent abuse in isolation.


The Police

The police have been involved in every aspect of solvent abuse from dealing with behaviour that disturbs the community to coping with the resulting accidents and sudden deaths that occurred. From the beginning, they sought to involve other agencies in the management of the associated problems and frequently became involved in community projects designed to offer recreational facilities to young people. They willingly participated in solvent abuse projects and have been instrumental in educating other groups about recognising solvent abuse and the associated dangers they discovered in the course of dealing with participants.

The police were also involved in prevention when they encouraged local shopkeepers to operate a voluntary ban on the sale of certain materials to young people. In Glasgow, where there are many small shops owned by Pakistanis, they sought and received, the co-operation of the Pakistan Social and Cultural Society in order to prevent the sale of glues to young people. During the early 1980s, this organisation invited police personnel to address the congregation in the mosque on more than one occasion. In addition, on their own initiative, the leaders of the Pakistani community circulated a letter in English and Asian languages requesting shopkeepers to 'treat all children as your own and let them live by refusing to sell any type of glue or solvent unless they are accompanied by a parent or guardian'.

## In-service Training

In-service training in Strathclyde has been organised for all professional groups involved in dealing with solvent abuse. Each group has organised its own programme according to its requirements. Special articles, pamphlets and news sheets have been prepared for professional organisations and groups. Seminars and lectures have been organised and resulted in overwhelming attendances because of the demand for information on the subject. There have been multi-disciplinary meetings and seminars in order to facilitate the exchange of information and attitudes on the subject

## The Information and Resource Unit on Addiction

Strathclyde Regional Social Work Department set up an Information and Resources Unit on Addiction in Glasgow in August 1982, initially for three years. It was funded by the Urban Aid Programme. Its aims were to increase the awareness of the public and the professional alike of the nature and severity of addiction problems and of the ways in which they can be recognised and resolved. To this end, it provides a comprehensive range of educational information on drugs, alcohol, solvents and gambling. Since its official opening in September

1982, its services have been extensively advertised.

## Local Government Responses

There was a brisk response on the part of Strathclyde Regional Council to solvent abuse from 1976 onwards. Between 1976 and 1978, the Officer/ Member Group on Addiction included solvent abuse in the range of addiction problems in which they maintained an interest. They reported great difficulty initially in getting everyone to recognise that the problem of children who were sniffing solvents was serious, but they were determined to tackle it even if this proved to be unpopular in some circles. In 1979, an Officer/Member Monitoring Group on Solvent Abuse was set up to decide on the best action to take in the interests of the children involved. By 1981, much concern was being expressed by the public about solvent abuse and the matter was receiving considerable coverage from the press. By this time, it was obvious to the many agencies involved that there were many different reasons for children abusing intoxicating vapours and a multiplicity of strategies had been tried with varying degrees of success by different agencies. Even the education of the public, the professionals and the children was considered to have been tackled in a variety of ways by different groups. The Monitoring Group believed that this had resulted in an excessive fragmentation of effort although many of the individual strategies were seen to be sound in themselves.

In April 1981, they set up a short-term working party to study the feasibility of formulating a corporate approach which would involve all agencies in more co-operative and consultative efforts and improve the co-ordination of the response to solvent abuse in Strathclyde.This working party consisted of the Principal Addiction Officer, the Deputy Director of Education, the Reporter to the Children's Panel, a chief superintendent of police and a member of the Chief Executive's Department.

The report of this group, <u>Solvent abuse - a corporate approach</u>, was published in April 1982. It was intended as a set of guidelines for the staff on the various agencies and departments involved in dealing with the problem as well as parents and the whole community of Strathclyde. The contents covered the identification of solvent abuse, its hazards, various intervention strategies, leaflets for parents and professionals, and guidelines for school staff, social workers and IT workers.[5] One notable feature was that it differentiated between the strategies that were appropriate for occasional, regular and chronic sniffers. It also included a review of approaches previously tried and a useful bibliography. The report recommended the establishment of multi-disciplinary groups at local level in districts where solvent abuse was a recognised problem and that these groups should consist of representatives from the caring agencies and any other local organisations likely to encounter the problem. The report further proposed that a representative from one of the caring agencies would act as local co-ordinator of resources and activities but that this would be in addition to existing duties and no additional staff would be employed. The suggested range of activities of the local groups included the provision of a central point offering information and assistance, the arranging of in-service training and the development of new strategies.

In March 1984, a review of the progress made towards implementing these guidelines specifically mentions the successful promotion of the preventive health education package for schools, already described, and the extensive use of leaflets for parents and professionals. 16 local corporate groups had been formed in various parts of Strathclyde but the review noted that this had not been the case in other areas where solvent abuse was prevalent. The multi-disciplinary group which had been formed in Lanark Division in January 1976 was still active and did not see the need for other groups to be formed. In Glasgow Division, a range of activities had already started when the report was published in 1982 and these continue to be pursued at present.

The ultimate success of the corporate approach will depend on the goodwill of the caring agencies, the priority which they give to the problems associated with solvent abuse and their ability to co-ordinate their activities with other agencies. Certainly, the corporate approach offers the hope that those individuals with the greatest problems will be able to obtain the help that they require.

## Conclusions

In Strathclyde, various groups were set up to deal with solvent abuse from 1976 onwards. When it became clear that there were a number of different reasons for solvent abuse and different degrees of involvement, a variety of community strategies was developed to cope with the range of problems. The most important of these were the treatment of acutely intoxicated cases, the long-term management of habitual abusers and the education of children, parents, professionals and public.

Although there was no difference of opinion concerning acute cases, there was a wide range of approaches to the management of abusers. The strategies initially adopted tended to depend on the nature of the agency involved rather than on the needs of the individual children. However, as the various degrees of involvement in solvent abuse became more fully understood, some groups attempted to distinguish between them and to devise strategies appropriate to individual needs. These methods of dealing with the problem are effective when applied to suitable cases but no one method can be used in every instance. There has been no real attempt to evaluate and compare the different approaches used.

The corporate approach in Strathclyde is an attempt to co-ordinate the original diversity of effort on a regional basis. Its ultimate success will depend on its ability to meet the varying needs of those who require help. This, in turn, can only be achieved by the capacity of the people in the caring role to recognise the needs of each individual and by the strength of their motivation to respond appropriately.

REFERENCES

1.  Cohen S. (1973), 'The volatile solvents',
Public Health Reviews, 2 (2) 185-214.
2.  Barnes  G.  (1979),  'Solvent  abuse:  a
review', International Journal of the Addictions,
14(1), 1-26.
3.  Stybel  L.J.  (1977),  'Psychotherapeutic
options in the treatment of child and adolescent
hydrocarbon inhalers', American Journal of Psychotherapy, 1V, 525-32.
4.  Sourindhrin  I.  and  Baird  J.  (1984),
'Management of solvent misuse: a Glasgow community
approach',  British  Journal  of  Addiction,  79,
227-32.
5.  Strathclyde  Regional  Council  (1982),
Solvent abuse: a corporate approach, Strathclyde
Regional Council, 1982.

Chapter Nine

THE NATIONAL RESPONSE

At both a Scottish and a British level, there have
been a number of actions with respect to solvent
abuse which have had some impact on the problem.
Some of these have been attempts to improve
knowledge and understanding of the various factors
which relate to the problem. These have included a
government-sponsored film for professionals and
readily available leaflets and pamphlets from the
Institute for the Study of Drug Dependence in
London intended for a wide range of people. In
Scotland, the Scottish Health Education Group
produced a guide to solvent abuse and research into
the nature and extent of the problem has been
carried out by the Social Work Services Group of
the Scottish Office. At a national level, four
major topics merit detailed discussion and this
chapter deals mainly with these. They are the
legislation proposed by central government for the
whole of the United Kingdom, the response by the
manufacturers to the problem, the prosecutions
under Scottish Law relating to solvent abuse and
the amendment to the Social Work (Scotland) Act of
1968 which made solvent abuse a cause for referral
of children found indulging in the practice.
    Before considering these matters, it is
worthwhile reviewing the steps taken in America to
cope with a similar problem. Solvent abuse started
earlier there and some of the options for dealing
with it, which might be thought to be worthwhile
for Britain, have already been tried in a number of
the states and cities of the USA. For example, New
York City introduced two laws to deal with glue
sniffing and the background to them is both
interesting and relevant.
    In 1963, the youth section of the New York
Police became aware of glue sniffing which was

184

considered to be hazardous to the health and safety
of youngsters. Police statistics, community groups
and the newspapers all confirmed that glue sniffing
among teenagers was an increasingly popular and
hazardous activity.[1] The Health Department of New
York City was involved in the problem and was
expected to take action of some kind.

In June 1963, a meeting was held involving the
manufacturers of 'Hobby Glue', officials of the
Hobby Industries Association and representatives of
various New York City departments. It was reported
to the meeting that the Health Department intended
to amend the Health Code but it was agreed that the
hobby industry, at its own request, could have one
month in which to act on the problem before the
introduction of any such changes. In the intervening
period, the Police Youth Division launched a huge
campaign about the dangers of glue sniffing and
asked for voluntary co-operation to reduce the
access of young people to glue. In spite of all
these efforts, the police statistics for glue
sniffing showed a dramatic increase and the numbers
involved more than doubled between 1962 and 1963.

In December 1963, representatives from the
Health Department Youth Division, the Police
Narcotics Bureau and the Police Legal Bureau met
and they recommended legislation for the following
reasons. Firstly, the manufacturers had not solved
the problem, and indeed, the numbers of youngsters
involved had increased rather than decreased.
Secondly, the police said that they could not
control the sale of glue to young people when there
was only a voluntary ban by some willing
shopkeepers. They said that they required legislation
and that this need was more urgent following two
deaths from glue sniffing. As a result of this
meeting two laws were passed for New York City.
These laws made it an offence to sell or provide
glue or solvent based cement to anyone under the
age of 18 unless it formed part of a model
construction kit. It also became an offence to sell
glue to anyone at all if the purpose of that person
was known or suspected to be intoxication. Sniffing
glue or possessing it with the intent to use it for
intoxication was also made a criminal offence.

By 1967 legislation had been enacted in count-
less cities and states of the United States.[2] The
statute legislation of Maine and Maryland made it a
criminal offence to inhale a variety of volatile
products and both states imposed a maximum punishment of eleven months' imprisonment for anyone

185

thus convicted. A further eight laws were
introduced in different states prohibiting 'sniffing'
itself as well as the possession of solvents and
the 'selling' of them. In some states, laws only
covered glues and this led to aerosol sniffing
instead with a resulting epidemic of sudden deaths.
There was an anomaly in the law in New York State
that made it possible to detain a boy, aged 16 to
21, for three years but a girl could only be held
for five days for the same offence. Massachusetts
permitted arrests without warrants and detention
for 24 hours of juveniles caught glue sniffing.
Illinois stated in its legislation that 'no person
shall breathe...any compound...containing...any
substance...for the purpose of changing...mental
processes'. It is not clear that this wide
definition does not ban the inhalation from
cigarettes and cigars, sniffing perfumes and
flowers and perhaps even breathing.

The legislation enacted in the different
states and cities consisted of 'sell' legislation
and 'smell' legislation. In California and
Maryland, there were also laws that made it
compulsory for the manufacturers to label all
products with a list of contents stating those that
might be misused by inhalation.[3] This enabled the
young people to identify the most harmful, and most
potent, substances very easily. In New York State,
Ohio and Texas, it was made a statutory requirement
that nauseous repellants should be added to glues.
For example, in New York State, 0.25 to 0.35 per
cent oil of mustard had to be added to glues as a
deterrent to would-be sniffers. However, in 1981,
studies of the effects of oil of mustard on rats
indicated that it might cause cancer. In February
1982 the legislation was rescinded and it was
removed from the glues lest it harm the legitimate
users of the products. Ohio and Texas had been
unable to find suitable substances to add to glues
so this step was not required.

There is no evidence to believe that any of
the 'sell' legislation had any influence on
controlling the problem. In states which legislated
against glue sniffing as such, there was a marked
trend towards the abuse of other volatile
substances which could still be bought legally. As
a result, there was a marked increase in the number
of sudden deaths caused, for example, by aerosols
which was opposite to the effect which the
legislators intended. In most cases, the 'smell'
legislation was unenforceable as the threat of

punishment was often an idle one. However, some researchers mentioned that the activity was being driven underground as fear of repercussions made children and parents alike reluctant to give information to the police or other agencies.

In a paper in 1967 entitled <u>Is legislation the answer?</u>, the director of the Criminal Law Project at the University of New York posed three questions relevant to legislation and solvent abuse.

1. Is solvent abuse a large enough problem in society to require government action?
2. If it is such a problem, does it require the intervention of the criminal law?
3. If the problem is criminalised, can an effective outcome be expected?

These questions neatly summarise the difficulties to be faced in attempting to deal with solvent abuse by criminalising any aspect of it.[3] A wide variety of such laws was tried in the United States but there is no evidence that there was any success in curtailing the practice or in helping children with difficulties.


Legislation in Britain

Successive British governments have shown interest in the subject of solvent abuse and the associated problems. Members of Parliament with seats in Lanarkshire raised the matter on a number of occasions in the House of Commons from the early 1970s followed by Glasgow MPs during the late 1970s. Since then, and especially in recent years, many other MPs from constituencies across the country have become involved. Scottish health ministers have taken an interest in the research projects and service programmes about solvent abuse in Strathclyde and have taken time and trouble to familiarise themselves with the trends of this practice. A similar interest in solvent abuse was shown at a political level in England and Wales.

In 1973, in reply to a question in the House of Commons regarding the banning of the sale of glue to children, the Secretary of State for Scotland said that such a ban was unjustified and impractical because of the small number of children involved in solvent abuse. Another attempt to ban sales was put to Parliament in 1976 but it was decided that the best way to tackle solvent abuse was by a health education programme in schools. In House of Commons debates in December 1981 and again in December 1983, shopkeepers who were operating voluntary restrictions on the sale of products containing solvents to young people were mentioned and congratulated. The Government subsequently drew up a voluntary set of guidelines for shopkeepers which was issued in January 1984 as a DHSS letter.[4]

In general, the government has adopted a low-key approach to the matter but, in 1984, a private member's bill, 'Limitation of Sales of Solvents Bill' was proposed for England, Wales and Northern Ireland.[5] It was designed to make it an offence for a person to sell or offer for sale substances to people under the age of 16 years if it was known or if there seemed to be reasonable grounds for believing that those substances were likely to be inhaled for intoxication. It was therefore aimed at retailers but was abandoned after its first reading.

'The Intoxicating Substances (Supply) Bill' 1984 was another private members bill aimed at curbing solvent abuse and had a broader application than the previous one.[6] Its intention was to prohibit the supply, to persons under the age of 18 years, of any substances which might cause intoxication if inhaled, provided that the supplier knows or has reasonable cause to suspect that the substance is going to be inhaled for intoxicating purposes. A person convicted of violating this law would be liable to imprisonment for up to six months or a fine of up to £2000. This bill covered not only glues but all substances which could be abused by inhalation for the purposes of intoxication. The Intoxicating Substances (Supply) Act became law for England, Wales and Northern Ireland in August 1985.

The problems associated with this type of legislation are likely to be that shopkeepers could find it difficult to judge the age of a would-be purchaser with reasonable accuracy and, in any case, children who are determined to indulge their habit can find suitable solvent-based materials at home. The average home would contain about 30 such products. Thefts from factories, hospitals, schools and elsewhere are likely to increase as was seen in Strathclyde when voluntary bans were brought into operation and it is reasonable to suppose that the same thing would occur in other parts of the country. Voluntary bans have been found to reduce the total number involved in solvent abuse but it is the casual users who stop while the habitual abusers turn to other sources. A final point worth mentioning is that the majority of children who use these products properly will find it almost impossible to buy them. Only time will tell what the outcome of this act will be.

Questions have been raised in the House of Commons from time to time regarding legislation which would make it an offence to be under the influence of intoxicating vapours. However, there has been general agreement about the undesirable features of such legislation since it would be likely to make those indulging in the practice more secretive than at present. It would also make it more difficult for people who are in need of help to ask for it because in doing so they would have to admit that an offence had been committed. At present parents in Scotland can go for help to a number of agencies including the police but if legislation existed which criminalised solvent abuse then they would be very reluctant to seek help. Therefore, those who most needed help would be least able to get it. It would also label people as criminal at an early age which is directly opposed to the philosophy behind the juvenile justice system in Scotland and could only be regarded as a retrograde step towards nineteenth-century attitudes. So far this has not happened instead solvent abuse has become a non-offence ground for referral to the Reporter under the Social Work (Scotland) Act as is discussed below.

There has already been discussion in Britain about the addition of noxious substances to some products as a way of deterring their abuse. This seemed to many people to be a simple solution to the problem but it is in fact, far from simple. Sir George Young is quoted in Hansard July 1980 as having asked the Chemical Defence Establishment to estimate the cost of developing a suitable additive for the most commonly abused substances.[7] The answer was that, at that particular time, the project would take about two and a half years, would cost £150,000 and had no guarantee of success. A private member's bill, 'Glue Abuse (Prevention) Bill' was drawn up requiring the addition, by manufacturers, of such substances to all glues on sale to the public. It was abandoned after its second reading.[8]

It seems fortunate that these glue additives have not been used in this country, particularly in view of the American experience that actions taken solely to prevent glue sniffing cause the abusers to turn to other available substances such as aerosols or butane, the abuse of which seems to be more dangerous and leads to an increase in the number of deaths. It would seem that sniffing glues rather than other substances is the least dangerous form of inhalant misuse. This is supported by the statistics from Strathclyde where sniffing glues has been by far the most common practice but has accounted for only about a third of the sudden deaths. It also seems that physical damage from the abuse of glues is quite rare. If legislation requiring the addition of deterrents is passed, it is logical that it should apply to those substances which most frequently cause death or deterrents must be added to all products capable of being abused.

## Response of the Manufacturers

By the mid-1970s, some manufacturers had responded to the growing public concern about solvent abuse by voluntarily reformulating their products. For example, trichloroethylene was sometimes replaced by toluene which is less harmfull.

In January 1979, one of the major adhesive manufacturers, Evode Ltd., issued information to all retailers about glue sniffing. This took the form of a staff notice giving salient facts, naming the products involved and indicating the signs to look for in young people. It pointed out that glue sniffing was not a criminal offence and suggested some practical ways of dealing with the problem. This information is still available.[9]

Many of the responses by manufacturers have been co-ordinated by the British Adhesives and Sealants Association (BASA) who appointed an executive director from one of its member companies with a remit to identify suitable initiatives and co-ordinate them into strategies to combat solvent abuse. BASA initiatives have included support for the DHSS film about solvent abuse and for research projects at St. George's Hospital in London.[10] Using DHSS guidelines as a model, BASA has published and distributed to shopkeepers a special leaflet and poster that describe how to identify glue sniffers and advise them of the right to decline to sell products to anyone suspected of intending to abuse them.[11] BASA intends to raise funds to support the solvent abuse counsellor of the

National Children's Bureau and is also funding a
number of informational projects connected with
solvent abuse. BASA regards solvent abuse as a
problem for society as a whole but is willing to
co-operate with other agencies in efforts to reduce
its extent.

Both Evode and Dunlop have developed water-based
adhesives which have many of the properties of
solvent-based adhesives but which, because the
water is non-intoxicating, cannot be used for glue
sniffing.[12] There is no doubt that this is partly
in response to the problem of solvent abuse.
However, there are other valid reasons for
developing and marketing these adhesives such as
the reduction of fire risks. Some have now been
available for several years although they have met
with some customer resistance. It should be noted
that the efforts to sell water-based adhesives have
resulted in them capturing approximately 75 per
cent of the total value of retail sales of
adhesives.

Members of the general public, professional
people and Members of Parliament often raise the
question about putting additives into products to
deter their abuse. To the uninitiated, this seems
to be a simple and obvious answer to a complicated
problem but, as has already been discussed, it is
very difficult in practice and it would cause a
number of major problems for the manufacturer.

There is a wide range of products that could
be abused for their intoxicating vapours including
petrol, fuel gases, aerosols of all kinds,
adhesives, nail polish remover, paints, paint
thinners, cleaning fluids, shoe conditioner, dyes
and many others. Many millions of people throughout
the world use these products correctly and safely
in their daily lives. Only a very small minority of
young people abuse them as intoxicating agents and
many of them do it on a few occasions only and then
stop. As even smaller proportion go on to abuse the
vapours on a chronic long-term basis and these
individuals will change brands or even the type of
product in order to sustain their habit if their
favourite product is no longer available. These
individuals would also be more likely to move on to
the abuse of other substances such as alcohol or
drugs if all volatile substances became unavailable
to them or if they had been modified to produce
unpleasant side-effects. The manufacturer is
therefore faced with the problem of finding a
suitable substance which, when added, will deter

sniffing but at the same time would not deter or harm the normal user. Even if this can be done, society is still faced with the problem of the chronic abusers who will not be changed by adding deterrent substances but will probably just move on to some other form of drug abuse.

In the United States, where additives have been tried, the most commonly used was allyl isothiocyanate, often called oil of mustard. This is an oily liquid which causes irritation in its concentrated form and when inhaled it produces watery eyes, sneezing, irritation of the lungs and vomiting. It presents the manufacturer with a number of problems such as the risk to industrial workers engaged in the manufacture of glues, possible weakening of the bonding strength of the glue and a reduction in the efficacy of the additive during storage of the glue after manufacture. The long-term health risks to humans are not known but allyl isothiocyanate has produced cancer in rats exposed to it which suggests that there is a risk to anyone who, for legitimate purposes, uses large quantities of glues containing this additive. One manufacturer in Britain has been adding oil of mustard to tubes of polystyrene cement, an adhesive used in model making. The company uses synthetic oil of mustard rather than the natural form which is thought to cause cancer and reports that it has been accepted by the customers.[13]

After a short period of continuous sniffing the irritating effect is said to be quite pronounced. However, there are still many practical difficulties for the manufacturers. If irritants were to be added on a voluntary basis by some, but not all manufacturers, the former might find themselves at a disadvantage since the legitimate users would probably prefer the brands without any unpleasant deterrent. If irritants were added only to certain types of products, for example glues, then abusers would simply switch to other types so that all products likely to be abused would have to be treated and it would be difficult to find an additive suitable for everything. The legitimate users of all these products would also find the additives unpleasant and there would probably be pressure for their removal. Imagine if nail varnish were vile-smelling or household paints gave off an offensive and irritating vapour. Consider the difficulties and cost of adding a deterrent to the enormous quantity of petrol used each year.[13]

Adding deterrents would be costly and this must be passed on to the customer who, even without the additional cost, would probably prefer not to have them in many of the products that we all need in our everyday lives.

## Scottish Prosecutions Relating to Solvent Abuse

A number of legal cases involving various aspects of solvent abuse have been heard in Scotland and the response of the Scottish legal system to the various problems which have arisen is interesting.

The case of Fisher v. Keane in 1979 involved the prosecution of an individual for breach of the peace on account of glue sniffing.[14] The legal question which it raised was whether glue sniffing in itself could be considered a breach of the peace. The details are as follows. One evening in 1979, two police constables were stopped by a woman in a state of alarm and agitation who told them that she had seen a youth who was sniffing glue and said that he should be stopped. The complainant refused to give her name. The youth seemed to be inhaling from a bag and, when approached by the two constables, was found to have a dazed expression and seemed oblivious to his surroundings. He was cautioned, charged with breach of the peace and subsequently found guilty by the Sheriff. At the appeal against his conviction, counsel for the defence criticised the Sheriff and said that the real basis of the conviction was that the accused had been sniffing glue which was not an offence. It was claimed that the conclusion drawn by the Sheriff, that there had been a breach of the peace, was based on two factors. These were that the Sheriff had inferred from his own knowledge of glue sniffing and its effects, and from the statement of an unknown woman that a breach of the peace had occurred. This was not based on evidence presented in court that the lieges (public) had been alarmed or upset. In order to be convicted of breach of the peace, the glue sniffer's conduct had to be of such a nature as to have caused alarm to the lieges or at least to have been such that it might be reasonably expected to have led to the lieges being alarmed or upset. The conviction was quashed.

A similar case was that of Taylor v. Hamilton (unreported) which again arose from a breach of the peace. Evidence was presented that the two accused youths had been observed in May 1983 on a footpath by a member of the public. They had been sniffing glue from plastic bags and were staggering, swaying and walking round in circles. It was proved during the trial that the woman who complained to the police had been alarmed because she had seen glue sniffing before and was aware of the associated health hazards and uncontrolled behaviour. She also feared that her children might be affected. The Sheriff convicted the two accused on the charge of breach of the peace. The appeal was heard in October 1984 in the High Court of Justiciary and was refused as being without merit. In this case, the glue sniffing itself was not an offence but the alarm caused by the behaviour of the accused while intoxicated meant that a breach of the peace had been committed.

Under Section 5(1) of the Road Traffic Act 1972, it is an offence to drive a vehicle on the roads while 'unfit to drive through drink or drugs'. In the Glasgow case of Duffy v. Tudhope, heard in 1983, the drug was toluene.[15] The circumstances were as follows.

A man was seen driving a van in a very erratic fashion during the early hours of the morning and was eventually stopped by the police. A strong smell of glue was detected in the van and a tin of adhesive lay beside the driver's seat. A strong smell of glue came from the man's breath, he seemed confused, his memory was poor and his speech was incoherent. He was charged in the Sheriff Court in Glasgow that he had driven the van while unfit to drive through drink or drugs contrary to Section 5(1) of the Road Traffic Act. He was convicted but appealed to the High Court on the grounds that toluene (from glue) was not a drug because it had no medicinal purpose. The case went to the Appeal Court who considered the English case of Bradford v. Wilson[16] in which there was a similar trial for contravention of Section 5(1) of the Road Traffic Act involving driving while under the influence of toluene from glue. The appeal hearing, at the Queen's Bench Division in March 1983, held that a substance did not need to be a medicine in order to be a drug within the meaning of the act. It was considered that a drug is not only something which is taken by injection or by mouth but may also include a substance which is inhaled. The Scottish Appeal Court in September 1983 similarly held that any material which has a drugging effect on the driving capacity of a driver is a drug for the purposes of Section 5(1) of the Road Traffic Act and the appeal was dismissed since toluene fitted this definition. Therefore, it is possible for individuals to be convicted of being unfit to drive while impaired due to toluene.

The Scottish legal system remains basically a common law system at least as far as the most serious crimes are concerned and can therefore be considered to be very much a matter of common sense. It is different from the English system which is based on statute law. The strength of Scottish Common Law in criminal matters is that it is not static but can be adapted in certain circumstance to meet novel situations. It has not apparently been weakened by the passage of time and the flexibility of Scottish Law has been applied in some cases involving solvent abuse.

The case of <u>Skeen v. Malik</u> was heard in the Sheriff Court of Glasgow and Strathkelvin in August 1977. A shopkeeper was charged with wilfully, culpably and recklessly selling to various children and young people aged 12 to 16 years quantities of a household glue knowing that they were buying the cans and tubes for the purpose of intoxication to the danger of their health and lives. A plea was taken as to whether or not such a complaint was relevant under Scottish Law.[17] This objection on the grounds of relevancy was upheld and the Sheriff stated a case for the opinion of the High Court. This case went no further as the Crown then abandoned it.

Another similar case, that of <u>Khaliq and Ahmed v. Her Majesty's Advocate</u>, occurred in 1983. It involved two Glasgow shopkeepers who were accused of wilfully and recklessly supplying to a number of children under the age of 16 years, quantities of solvents in or together with containers such as tins, tubes, crisp-packets and plastic bags for the purpose of inhaling vapours of the solvents from the containers. It was claimed that they did this knowing that the children intended to use the solvents and containers for that purpose and that the inhalation by them of the vapours was or could be injurious to their health and dangerous to their lives.[18]

The case had been considerably investigated and prepared by the Community Involvement Branch of the Police, the Procurator Fiscal's Office in Glasgow and the Crown Office in Edinburgh. Eighteen young people, aged 8 to 15 years were involved in the case and it was alleged that they had bought glue and been sold it or another solvent in tins, tubes, crisp-packets and plastic bags. The two shopkeepers were also accused of reset with respect to certain items that they had taken from the children in exchange for glue. Previously, the police, social workers, parents and local councillors had all made repeated visits to the shop but had failed to persuade the brothers to stop selling glue sniffing kits to children. A public demonstration was held outside the shop but again there was no result. Similarly, attempts by the leaders of the Asian community had no effect. Finally, the authorities decided to take action.

Originally the trial was set for September 1983 but an objection was raised by the defence that the Crown was attempting to create a new law in Scotland. It is worth noting at this point that the High Court of Justiciary in Scotland still retains the power to create new crimes for which people may be prosecuted. The Crown contended that the charges in this case did not constitute a new crime and that supplying glue sniffers was a modern example of conduct which Scottish Law had long regarded as criminal. The original trial judge, Lord Avonside, stated that the charge was relevant. The defence referred this decision to the Court of Criminal Appeal and the appeal was heard before the Lord Justice General (the most senior Scottish judge) sitting with Lords Cameron and Dunpark. The appeal was refused and the charge held to be relevant. The charge proceeded at common law and in December 1983 the two shopkeepers pleaded guilty at their trial. They were sentenced to three years imprisonment but, on appeal, this was reduced to two years. This case was considered to be novel in Scottish Criminal Law. It involved the application of ancient common law to a new situation.

In December 1984, in a similar case, another shopkeeper from Glasgow was found guilty of selling glue sniffing kits to teenagers and was sentenced to imprisonment for 18 months.

In 1984, a man was charged in England with offences contrary to Sections 22 and 24 of the Offences against the Person Act of 1861. This act had not been used previously to prosecute persons for supplying solvents. The background to the case that relates to solvent abuse is that the accused invited young boys, aged 9 to 16 years into his house and encouraged them to indulge in practices that would not have been permitted at home. These included glue sniffing and petrol sniffing. Seven of the boys sniffed glue in the accused's house when he was present and he kept glue and bags in his house for the occasions when boys failed to bring their own supplies. In October 1984, at the Old Bailey, in the case of <u>Regina v. Braund</u>, the jury convicted the accused on a number of charges of 'administering a stupifying drug matter or thing contrary to Section 22 of the Offences against the Person Act 1861' to enable himself to commit an indictable offence and 'administering a noxious thing contrary to Section 24 of the Offences against the Person Act 1861' with intent to injure, aggrieve or annoy. He was also found guilty of indecent assault. The offences had occurred over a period of three years.

## The Solvent Abuse (Scotland) Act 1983

An outline of the Scottish system of juvenile justice is given in Appendix A and the reader who is unfamiliar with this system is referred to it. The Social Work (Scotland) Act 1968 is an integral part of this system and was framed with the intention of making provision for the social welfare of children in Scotland. Under Section 32(2)(a) of this act, a child could be deemed to be in need of compulsory measures of care if he or she is considered to be beyond the control of the parents. In the case of persistent detected solvent abuse, this section of the act could be used to refer a child to the Reporter to the Children's Panel. From the late 1970s, the Strathclyde Police adopted the practice of taking home children whom they had caught sniffing solvents and of requesting that their parents warn the children, in the presence of the police, about the dangers of their behaviour. If this happened on three separate occasions, the child could then be referred to the Reporter as being outwith parental control.
    However, this policy was regarded as inadequate by many people and a private member's bill, The Solvent Abuse (Scotland) Bill, was introduced by Mr David Marshall, the Member of Parliament for Shettleston, Glasgow. Mr Marshall explained the background to his bill to the House of Commons and said that it was not his intention to make solvent abuse a punitive offence but to introduce caring legislation. He pointed out that, in Scotland, the Children's Hearing system made it possible for children's problems to be discussed informally in the presence of the child and his parents. He reminded the House that Section 32(2) of the Social

Work (Scotland) Act specified the conditions which indicated that a child might need compulsory measures of care. His bill was designed to extend these conditions to include solvent abuse for which his definition was 'solvent abuse is inhalation for the purposes of intoxication or hallucination of glue, adhesive, the contents of aerosols or any product containing volatile substances'.

The Solvent Abuse (Scotland) Act 1983 received the Royal Assent on 13 May 1983 and its provisions came into force on 13 July 1983. This introduced a new subsection into the Social Work (Scotland) Act, Section 32(2)(gg) and enabled the Reporter to exercise the same discretion with regard to solvent abuse as he could with a number of other grounds. Firstly, he could take no action, secondly, he could refer the case for social work supervision of the child at home on a voluntary basis or, thirdly, he could arrange for a hearing by the Children's Panel on the grounds that the child might be in need of compulsory care.

Although this new subsection makes it possible for children who abuse solvents to be referred to the Reporter for an assessment of their need for compulsory care, only time will make clear what the outcome will be. Some of the children referred are likely to be known to the juvenile justice system for other reasons and some will need no further action. It is the cases which lie between these two extremes which will cause most difficulty. First the Reporter and then the members of the Children's Panel and social workers will have to decide on the best courses of action for these children and, to do so, will have to take account of the underlying problems and not just the solvent abuse on its own.

Clear guidelines will have to be set in order to identify the different categories of solvent abuse. It will be necessary to distinguish between, on one hand, the needy chronic abuser and, on the other hand, the normal child who has simply experimented briefly with solvents or who has been socially pressurised into occasional abuse.


Conclusions

Measures have been taken outside Strathclyde which are likely to affect solvent abuse locally. The most important of these have been discussed above. There might also seem to be a number of other tempting options but the consequences, or even the relevance, of any such action must be considered carefully. Since the USA first encountered solvent abuse several years before it appeared in this country, the American experience can be a very useful guide for predicting the outcome of some of the options which might still be tried here. In particular, they have tried a number of legislative measures to eliminate the abuse of solvents, principally by making it a crime or by banning the sale of solvents to young people. Neither of these measures, the so called 'smell' and 'sell' legislation, were successful because they seemed to be unworkable and in some cases they might even have made the problem worse by driving it underground or by causing the abusers to switch to a more dangerous kind of product. Legislation which required manufacturers to list the harmful ingredients in their products served merely as a guide to the would-be abuser. Requiring the addition of a deterrent chemical to glues proved to be technically difficult and was unpleasant and possibly dangerous for the legitimate user. In Britain, a number of similar measures have been discussed but many have already been tried in America and found wanting.

The Intoxicating Substances (Supply) Act, which recently became law, applies to England, Wales and Northern Ireland and is aimed at controlling the supply of intoxicating volatile substances to persons under the age of 18. It makes it an offence to supply such a substance to a young person but only if the supplier knows or suspects that it is to be abused for the purposes of intoxication. It would therefore seem to be aimed partly at those who might be tempted to exploit young people for profit by selling these substances to them so that they can indulge in solvent abuse. In this respect, it provides for England, Wales and Northern Ireland what already exists in Scotland because of Scottish Common Law. However, it is possible that it might have a number of undesirable effects. For example, the number of thefts of these substances from various premises might be expected to increase. Shopkeepers, fearing possible prosecution, might refuse to sell any glues or other substances with volatile components to all young people under the age of 18 even if there is no suspicion of solvent abuse. It might even be considered dangerous to sell petrol to a 17-year-old who has a driving licence and who owns a car or motorbike. This law could therefore be excessively restrictive to the majority of young people who never indulge in solvent abuse. Much will depend on the legal interpretation of this act and only time will allow an assessment of its success.

Legislation aimed at the manufacturer has also been discussed. It must be remembered that most manufacturers have already voluntarily removed the more harmful solvents from their products and that manufacturers of glues have developed water-based alternatives for many solvent-based glues. However, not all glues can be replaced with alternative solvent-free products which are satisfactory for every purpose. It has been proposed that manufacturers should be required to add deterrent substances to their products but, as has been described, there are many practical difficulties associated with this and the effect on the legitimate user would probably be undesirable and perhaps expensive. The range of products that would have to be treated in this way is so large that this strategy would be analogous to 'using a sledge hammer to crack a nut'. The author is of the opinion that this approach is not feasible and is the wrong way to tackle the problem.

From the legal point of view in Scotland, solvent abuse is not a crime but associated anti-social acts caused by intoxication such as alarming behaviour or driving a vehicle while under the influence of solvents can and have led to successful prosecutions. In this respect, the law seems to be able to cope with the unacceptable behaviour caused by solvent abuse without criminalising solvent abuse itself. This is particularly important because so many of those involved in solvent abuse are very young and might otherwise be labelled as deviant even if their association with the practice was only transient and experimental. If such young people were to be treated as criminals, it would go against the spirit of the Scottish system of juvenile justice which is intended to be caring rather than punitive. Because of the flexibility of Scottish common law, it seems to be possible to deal with the 'glue pushers', those who sell for profit to young people volatile substances for the purposes of intoxication, and the cases which have already been tried will hopefully do much to curtail this activity. There would therefore seem to be no need to introduce a Scottish equivalent to the Intoxicating Substances (Supply) Act.

The amendment to the Social Work (Scotland)

Act by the Solvent Abuse (Scotland) Act 1983
permits solvent abuse to be a specific reason for
referral of a child to the Reporter as someone who
might be in need of community care. However, it
would be unfortunate if solvent abuse alone was to
be considered in these cases and if every child
referred in this way was 'treated' only for solvent
abuse. The chronic sniffer is likely to have
underlying problems of which the solvent abuse is
often a symptom and, in any case, many of these
young people are likely to be known to the system
because of other behaviour. On the other hand, the
experimental and social abuser will usually not
require any kind of extensive intervention. If this
amendment is to be effective, it is desirable that
the members of the Children's Panel and social
workers have clear guidelines that allow them to
differentiate between the types of abusers. If this
amendment leads to further action in cases of
chronic solvent abuse which were previously
undetected, it will have proved to be very valuable
indeed for the people who need help most.

REFERENCES

1. Davis, R.F. (1967), 'The New York City experience', Juvenile Court Judges Journal, 18, 53-5.

2. Lewis, P.W. and Patterson, D.W. (1974), 'Acute and chronic effects of the voluntary inhalation of certain commercial volatile solvents by juveniles', Journal of Drug Issues, Spring, 162-70.

3. Mueller, G.O.W. (1967), 'Is legislation the answer?', Juvenile Court Judges Journal, 18, 59-63.

4. Department of Health and Social Security (1984), Guidelines for the sale of solvent-based products, January 12 1984.

5. Hansard, 'Limitation of Sale of Solvents Bill No. 172', H.C. Bill presented, first reading, Vol. 59, col 742 (8th May 1984).

6. Hansard, 'Intoxicating Substances (Supply) Bill', H.C. Deb., second reading, Vol. 71, col 641-85 (18th January 1985).

7. Hansard, 'Glue sniffing', H.C. Deb., Vol. 989, col 203-15 (21st July 1980).

8. Hansard, 'Glue Abuse (Prevention) Bill No. 165', H.C. Deb. second reading, Vol 59, col 362 (2nd May 1984).

9. Evode Ltd., (1979), Glue sniffing, Letter to all Evo-stik retailers.

10. British Adhesives and Sealants Association (1984), Facts Sheet - Solvent Abuse.

11. British Adhesives and Sealants Association (1984), Solvent Abuse - advisory kit, Published as a supplement to Hardware Trade Journal, June 29 1984.

12. British Adhesives and Sealants Association (1984), Non-sniffable adhesives, personal communication 13 December 1984.

13. British Adhesives and Sealants Association (1984), Aversive additives, personal communication, 17 and 21 December 1984.

14. Fisher v. Keane, Scots Law Times (notes) 28 (1981)

15. Duffy v. Tudhope, Scots Law Times, 107 (1984).

16. Bradford v. Wilson, Criminal Law Reports, 482, (1983).

17. Gane, C.H.W. and Stoddart, C.N. (1980). A casebook on Scottish Criminal Law. Assault and real injury, Chapter 10, p.316, W.Green and Son, Edinburgh.

18. <u>Khaliq and Ahmed v. Her Majesty's Advocates</u>, Scots Law Times, <u>137</u> (1984).

Chapter Ten

CONCLUSIONS

In writing this overview of solvent abuse in
Strathclyde, the author has sought to present a
community problem within a wider context. Solvent
abuse has been described as a modern epidemic but
the practice of inhaling intoxicating substances to
alter psychological states is not new and could be
as old as man himself. In modern society, petrol
sniffing came to attention in America in the 1950s
and glue sniffing in the 1960s. Children and
adolescents in many parts of the world are now
thought to have indulged in the practice since
then.

In Strathclyde, in the West of Scotland,
solvent abuse was first noticed in 1970 in
Lanarkshire and subsequently in Glasgow and
elsewhere a few years later. Detailed information
about the practice has been collected in Strathclyde
over the years by a number of people from different
agencies. In particular, details have accumulated
about the nature and extent of the practice, the
people involved and their reasons for involvement.
Information has been gathered gradually about the
acute and long-term effects of the practice and the
associated deaths. Various strategies have been
developed within and outside Strathclyde in
response to solvent abuse.

Many substances in common domestic and
industrial use have been found to be abused because
of their intoxicating effects but the most
frequently abused products have been proprietary
brands of glues although there have been recent,
unconfirmed reports of an increase in the use of
aerosols and butane. It has been found that if one
substance or brand is unavailable for any reason,
another can easily be found as a substitute. The
misuse of these products has been directly linked

to their ready availability and the fact that they are cheap to buy or easy to steal. However, despite this availability and low cost, there is no evidence that solvent abuse has been a significantly large problem among young people in Strathclyde in comparison for example with alcohol. There are no accurate data for estimating the extent of solvent abuse but it is thought that between one and ten per cent of all juveniles in Strathclyde may have been involved at some time. A larger proportion of children may have been involved from time to time among specific groups in certain residential establishments or in some schools. However, despite public and professional anxieties that the practice might become common and widespread, it seems clear that most young people have never been involved.

Solvent abuse in Strathclyde has involved teenagers, especially those aged between 13 and 15 years, more being boys than girls. The practice was found to be commoner in urban than in rural areas and, although it is not confined to areas of urban deprivation, it is more prevalent there. Individuals are involved in the practice in groups in much the same way as young football supporters or teenage drinkers. The single most important factor determining the onset of solvent abuse is probably peer group pressure. Any child who is curious and whose friends are involved is likely to 'have a go'. For the most part, involvement is transient or sporadic rather than regular. The factors leading to long-term chronic abuse are likely to come from deep psychological needs rather than from pressure exerted by the peer group. Solitary sniffing, like solitary drinking, is most unusual and should alert professionals to the likelihood of underlying problems.

Three groups of sniffers have been identified. The largest consists of the experimenters who try solvent abuse on a few occasions, satisfy their curiosity and then stop. Other reasons for their stopping could be dizziness or nausea experienced while sniffing, parental discovery, discouragement from peers or a talk from a well-liked youth leader. This group has minimal and transient involvement and usually indulges in groups. The individuals show no disturbance of function or behaviour.

The second group consists of those who might be called social sniffers in the same way that some adults are called social drinkers. They are involved sporadically rather than regularly or, if they are involved regularly, it tends to be on an infrequent basis. They almost always indulge in group sniffing thus maintaining their social contacts and relationships. They frequently complain of being bored and if more pleasant or acceptable activities are offered, the abuse stops dramatically. Because peer group pressure maintains the practice in these cases, they graduate from it in time as their friends move on to some new activity.

The third group represents only about 10 per cent of all cases seen by the author in Strathclyde. Starting as sporadic abusers, they indulge more frequently, regularly and repeatedly over periods of months or years. Unlike the others, they indulge alone or continue the practice with other chronic sniffers rather than stop when their original friends have done so. They eventually drop out of school and spend hours of each day in an intoxicated state. Their relationships suffer and they seem to live in an isolated chemical world of their own. Their repeated involvement is caused by psychological need and not social pressure.

The immediate effects of solvent abuse were found to be very similar to those associated with alcohol intoxication. However, the onset of intoxication and the subsequent recovery is quicker than with alcohol and hallucinations were reported by some young people. It might be expected that intoxication and hallucinations could lead to accidents or other adverse events and these were reported by a small number of people who were all habitual sniffers.

Of 335 young people seen in acute situations, only 2 per cent reported having had an accident while intoxicated and only 3 per cent had been admitted to hospital due to coma following solvent abuse. A further 14 per cent admitted to occasional blackouts while abusing solvents although they had all recovered rapidly and had not required hospital treatment. Although these estimates are subjective, they suggest a relatively low level of risk associated with acute episodes of solvent abuse and this is confirmed by statistics from Lanarkshire and Glasgow hospitals where the number of cases presenting due to solvent abuse is small. The hospital figures also confirm that the low level of risk does not only apply to those individuals who were detected but to all solvent abusers.

A study of possible long-term effects of solvent abuse was carried out in the course of

which almost 800 young people were thoroughly
investigated by the author. This involved full
medical examinations and blood tests for kidney and
liver function. Although the range of involvement
varied considerably, 13 per cent of those seen
could be considered to be chronic sniffers who had
indulged regularly for at least six months.
However, irrespective of their involvement in the
practice, none showed any evidence of physical
damage to their organ systems which could be
attributed to solvent abuse and none died during
the study. Therefore, it is possible to say that
there were no short or long-term toxic effects from
solvents in these cases. However, during the same
period, four young people, aged between 13 and 15
years, were known to have developed damage to
liver, kidney or brain function while sniffing,
regularly or sporadically, glues containing
toluene. Two of these recovered completely, one
made a partial recovery but continued to have
occasional fits and the fourth recovered some
function but had residual difficulties with
balance.

Long-term psychological effects were found
only among the habitual abusers. All developed
tolerance to solvents and a small number had also
developed psychological dependence. Nightmares,
headaches, impairment of concentration and memory
were found in some cases but the cause is not
understood.

All chronic sniffers had behaviour problems at
home and sometimes outside the home. Indeed, the
diagnosis of solvent abuse in this group was often
made by the parents who noted changes in their
children's pattern of behaviour. This is not a
specific sign of solvent abuse, since difficult
behaviour patterns during adolescence are common
while solvent abuse is not. None of the experimental
or social sniffers were in trouble at home because
of their behaviour.

In Strathclyde, 41 deaths associated with
solvent abuse occurred between 1970 and 1984. They
happened unpredictably and infrequently and nothing
is known about the extent of involvement of these
individuals before death although in a few cases
there appears to have been little or no prior
involvement. The simple, reliable methods which
were developed for identifying and measuring
solvents proved to be of great value in investigating
these cases. It is significant that more than
two-thirds of the deaths involved substances other

than glues and that the deaths tended to occur when the individual was alone. The implication from the first of these statements is that, although glues are not harmless, they are less likely to be associated with fatalities than other substances. Some of the methods employed when abusing butane and aerosols are more likely to prove fatal than inhaling toluene vapour from a small bag. Group sniffing seems to provide a measure of protection but even in such cases the others in the group have been known to run away rather than run for help if an emergency occurred.

The subject of deaths is a particularly emotive one. Each death is a personal tragedy for all those associated with the individual, particularly the family and friends. At a community level it is also a tragedy but one which fortunately is rare when compared with the number of people exposed to solvent abuse. According to statistics from the Greater Glasgow Health Board, there are fewer deaths among young people from solvent abuse than from acute alcoholic poisoning and the number of solvent abuse deaths is insignificant in comparison to the number of young people killed by accidents. This places solvent abuse in an appropriate perspective as a cause of death in young people.

The study indicated that there was a low level of accidents, coma and fatalities among glue sniffers. No evidence was found for long-term organic damage in a sample of almost 800 sniffers or in the 41 cases who died. In general, apart from a few rare cases of damage caused by adverse reactions or death in acute incidents, risks associated with solvent abuse seem to occur mainly among the habitual sniffers

These facts about solvent abuse have important implications for education and management. The information given about the problem must be appropriate to the people for whom it is intended. Factual details about the numbers involved in the practice, the different substances and methods used, the variation in the degree of involvement and the low level of associated risk are valuable for professional people and useful for reassuring large numbers of concerned parents at a public meeting. However, information of this kind is inappropriate and counter-productive for the parents of the habitual sniffer or of a child who has just had an accident or died. They need sympathetic handling which takes account of their feelings about the matter, some explanation of underlying problems and practical advice about where to go for professional assistance.

The educational strategies employed to prevent children from starting to experiment with solvent abuse are best left to those who educate children. The current approach of Strathclyde schools seems to be sensible. Firstly, it benefits from an integrated health education programme in the schools. Secondly, in schools where the head teacher considers solvent abuse to be an appropriate topic, the specially designed Strathclyde package about solvent abuse can be introduced into the overall programme. Thirdly, this programme includes educational packages intended to develop individual skills such as decision-making and this may be of benefit to potential habitual abusers by helping them to cope with some of their personal problems.

For the people who have to deal with individuals who abuse solvents, accurate information is essential in the opinion of the author. There is no point in trying to frighten children who may know more about solvent abuse than the professional people who are looking after them. Telling them that most people who indulge come to no harm but that some have accidents or go into a coma is honest and sensible. Frightening and exaggerated stories are unlikely to be believed and might prejudice the relationship between the child and the professional. There is a place for some advice on first-aid and on the dangers of solitary sniffing. There is also a case for education to reduce the risks to the habitual abuser if he cannot be prevailed upon to give up the practice immediately. For example, it is sensible to take any opportunity to persuade these individuals to switch from butane or aerosols to glue and at the same time have them adopt less hazardous methods and reduce their exposure to solvents. This is not an appropriate strategy for children who are not involved in solvent abuse and is not recommended for the occasional sniffer who is abusing only glues. In such cases, this approach might stimulate non-sniffers to start solvent abuse and encourage casual sniffers to experiment with some of the more dangerous substances as a form of risk taking.

In relation to the management of the practice, it is crucial to distinguish between the three types of solvent abuser. Experimenters are likely to stop on their own because their curiosity is satisfied or because they found the practice

209

unpleasant. In other cases, a chat from their
parents, a youth leader or a teacher might suffice.
The social sniffers will almost always stop
sniffing when their group becomes involved in more
interesting and positive activities. Many youth
club leaders and intermediate treatment workers in
Strathclyde found that solvent abuse per se often
disappeared of its own accord, particularly if
other youth activities were introduced.

Management of chronic cases, on the other
hand, is difficult and long-term. No one agency can
be expected to have the answer probably because
there is no single answer. Dealing with chronic
sniffers in groups has been found to be ineffective
and chronic abusers seem to need an individual
approach in each case since they usually have
multiple difficulties. The exact interaction and
time-scale of individual, peer group and family
factors in the development of habitual solvent
abuse is not clear. What is clear is that, as long
as these difficulties remain unresolved, the
chronic abuser might be persuaded to give up
solvent abuse but is likely to turn instead to the
abuse of alcohol or drugs.

The needs of these individuals are many and
varied. After identifying habitual abuse, the first
requirement is to assess these needs. The
Strathclyde corporate approach placed emphasis on
the assessment of each case at a local level with a
subsequent referral, as appropriate, to a range of
therapeutic options but depends on the availability
of the necessary clinics. It seems, to the author,
that the person who should be involved in this
assessment and subsequent decisions on management
is someone with whom the child has a trusting
relationship. This might be a guidance teacher, an
intermediate treatment worker, a social worker, a
school nurse or a general practitioner. In some
cases, the ideal approach will involve family
therapy by a team of psychiatrists, psychologists
and social workers so that individual and family
factors might be evaluated and a rational
management scheme planned. Any necessary investigations should be carried out and these might include
a general physical examination, an examination of
the central nervous system and a psychological and
psychiatric evaluation. The overall programme in
these cases would include group sessions with all
members of the family and for the individual
concerned might involve behaviour modification,
development of social skills, diversionary

Conclusions

activities, remedial teaching and psychotherapy as
appropriate.

However, there are several problems associated
with this approach. There is a lack of centres
offering family therapy and also family therapy
sessions would be likely to extend over six to
twelve months. The children and their parents would
therefore need to be very motivated to continue to
attend for this period. Lack of motivation on the
part of the child can be a problem and sometimes
parents want help but believe that the basic
problem is solvent abuse rather than admit that it
is just one of a series of family difficulties.

If family therapy is not appropriate or if
suitable facilities are lacking, habitual sniffers
might benefit from clinics like the 'drop-in
clinic' in the East End of Glasgow which is
multi-disciplinary in its approach and which offers
many treatment programmes including psychotherapy,
play therapy , art therapy and help with reading.
However, in these cases, continuing social work
support in the community is essential. The exact
treatment programme must be tailored to the needs
of each individual whatever these might be and the
emphasis should be on the individual's overall
problems of which the solvent abuse might be the
least important. However, solvent abuse can
complicate the management and the ultimate
objective of the programme must be to ensure that
the solvent abuse ceases. Any treatment programme
which increases self-esteem, promotes family
relationships and encourages alternative activities
is likely to increase the chance of a successful
outcome.

The new subsection of the Social Work
(Scotland) Act now enables children to be referred
to the Reporter because of solvent abuse. Any
subsequent recommendations about residential
assessment or voluntary social work supervision
must depend not on the solvent abuse as such but on
the underlying problems. Various individuals known
to the author have been referred to assessment
centres in Strathclyde because of solvent abuse and
related behaviour problems and all have ultimately
improved. One noticeable feature of these young
people was that, after leaving the assessment
centre, they moved from home to live elsewhere as
soon as possible. It is not known if family therapy
would have produced different results in these
cases.

The actions taken by the Scottish legal system

Figure 10.1: Juvenile Population Age 10 - 19 years - Risk Factors

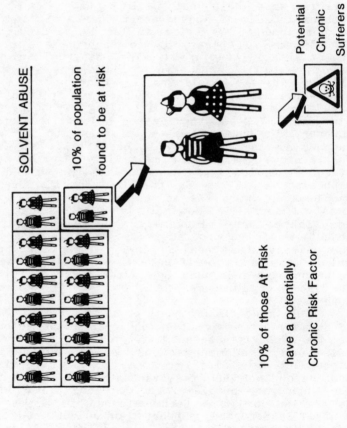

SOLVENT ABUSE

10% of population
found to be at risk

10% of those At Risk
have a potentially
Chronic Risk Factor

Potential
Chronic
Sufferers

with regard to driving under the influence of
solvents, the reckless supplying of solvents to
young people and breach of the peace while under
the influence of solvents seem to be appropriate.
It is doubtful if any further government legislation
is needed to improve the situation in Scotland.
Manufacturers have also taken positive action to
reduce the dangers from abuse of their products and
it is doubtful if they could do more without
causing a great deal of expense and inconvenience
to the public which would be out of proportion to
the size of the problem.

Although much valuable information on solvent
abuse has been collected in Strathclyde, there are
still gaps in the knowledge about certain aspects
of the problem. There is a need for further study
of the actual effects of different solvents on the
body with particular emphasis on determining the
length of time during which they are retained by
the brain fats. It is essential to investigate the
extent of impairment of concentration and memory in
habitual solvent abusers and to determine whether
these symptoms are directly attributable to
solvents. Accurate, detailed information on adverse
reactions of liver, kidney and brain should be
collected, if possible, at a national level. The
national mortality study has meant that details of
all deaths associated with solvent abuse have been
collected and this information is essential for the
development of central strategies.

Evaluation of educational programmes to
counter solvent abuse among children should be
undertaken. The outcome of different management
techniques for habitual solvent abusers should be
assessed to determine which are the most effective
in different types of cases.

While solvent abuse must surely be accepted as
part of the wider aspect of drug and alcohol abuse,
it is essential to keep in mind the fact that most
children and young people will never, at any time,
in any circumstances, experiment with substances
containing solvents (Figure 10.1). It is also
reassuring that most of those who do so will regard
it as a passing phase. In dealing with the
unfortunate few who become chronically involved,
there are three vital recommendations.

1.  Ensure that the professional people or
    agencies offering help are known in the
    community.

2. Ensure that children and families in need can find this help quickly and easily.
3. Keep solvent abuse in perspective as a small but important part of a much larger cluster of problems.

Finally, this overview of solvent abuse would seem to have established a need for further investigation of the problem to increase our understanding of its underlying causes. It is crucial that it is treated not as an isolated problem but as one which is similar to and associated with other chronic substance abuse. More detailed information is therefore required on addictive behaviour in general to gain insight into dealing with the long-term consequences of solvent abuse. Society's role must surely be to identify the victims and to treat them with competence and compassion.

Appendix A.

THE JUVENILE JUSTICE SYSTEM IN SCOTLAND

It is relevant to several sections of this book to outline the community system in Scotland for dealing with children who are delinquent or who are in need of care since this system differs in some important respects from the one which operates in England and Wales.[1]

There is nothing new about children who are delinquent or who need the protection of the community since there have always been such children. During the early part of the nineteenth century, children over the age of seven could be put to work like adults and, like adults, they could be tried and sentenced by the judiciary system provided that it could be proved that they knew the difference between right and wrong. The age of criminal responsibility was therefore seven years. Later in the nineteenth century, a different judiciary system with different methods of sentencing children was proposed by a number of people with progressive ideas. By the turn of the century, laws had been introduced throughout Europe to protect children from abuse and to establish special courts which subjected children to a less traumatic system of justice than that provided in the adult courts. Children who committed offences and children in need of care and protection both came under the jurisdiction of the same system.

At the end of the Second World War, a massive programme of social reform was launched in Britain. In the early years of this period juvenile crime fell only to rise again so that public concern was aroused and there began to be demands for action to deal with the increased crime. It was clear that the current state of the Scottish legal system, resting as it did on the sheriff courts, burgh courts, Section 50 courts and Justice of the Peace courts, each with different procedures and powers, had become too piecemeal. The McBoyle Committee was formed in 1961 to study the local authority provisions for neglected children. The Kilbrandon Committee was appointed in the same year to study the treatment of both juvenile delinquents and children who were in need of care and protection and to make appropriate recommendations. The Mc Boyle Committee reported its findings in 1963 and the Kilbrandon Committee in 1964.

The Kilbrandon Committee proposed a new system of juvenile justice, which would act in the best interests of the children and would remove from adult courts juvenile offenders and non-offenders who were under the age at which compulsory education ended.[2] The only exceptions were to be children who were prosecuted by the Lord Advocate of Scotland on account of exceptionally grave crimes such as murder or rape. The traditional crime and punishment approach was rejected in favour of a welfare attitude to children. It was hoped to look at the needs of the individual child by means of informed assessment and it was intended that there should be no distinguishing of need on the basis of offence or non-offence. Among the recommendations of the Kilbrandon report was one which proposed the formation of an integrated system involving a new public body called the Children's Panel, a new administrator of the system called the Reporter and a new agency called the Social Work Department. These recommendations were introduced into Scotland after the Social Work (Scotland) Bill received its final approval in the House of Commons and became law in July 1968. The Scottish system for dealing with juveniles who have committed an offence or who are in need of care and protection is defined by this act and is not the same as the system in England and Wales.

Even before the introduction of this act, the police in Scotland did not prosecute offenders directly, adult or juvenile, but referred cases to the Procurator Fiscal for assessment and, if appropriate, for subsequent prosecution. After the Social Work (Scotland) Act was passed, the Reporter became the person to whom individual juvenile cases were referred for a decision on how to proceed. The Reporter is the administrator of the new system and the adviser on law and procedures. In Scotland, there are 97 reporters, deputies and assistants. Some are legally qualified and some have a background of social work experience. Referrals to the Reporter may be made by the police, social workers, educational establishments, voluntary and statutory agencies or individuals.

There are certain categories of grounds for referral to the Reporter under the Social Work (Scotland) Act and the Reporter will act on information received from the police, from the Social Work Department and from schools. On the basis of this information the Reporter may decide.

1. To take no action.
2. To recommend voluntary social work supervision.
3. To refer the child to a Children's Panel for a decision about compulsory supervision.

In effect, the Reporter is the equivalent for juveniles of the Procurator Fiscal in the system of adult justice.

Panel members are appointed by the Secretary of State for Scotland from a list of applicants nominated for an area by the Children's Panel Advisory Committee, a regional committee set up for the purpose of recruiting and selecting new panel members. The panel consists of laymen selected on the grounds of knowledge and experience as being especially qualified to deal with the problems of children. They were to be chosen from a wide variety of occupations and income groups and were to be trained to take on the bulk of the work previously dealt with by the children's courts. The 'Panel' itself was not to be a court of law. The event at which an individual case is considered is termed a hearing and this is a meeting of a group of three panel members with the child, parents, social worker and Reporter. The group of panel members must include a person of each sex and one member acts as chairperson. There are 900 panel members in Strathclyde. The options open to a hearing are:

1. to discharge the child with no further contact.
2. to leave the child at home under the supervision of the Social Work Department to await a later review or,
3. to make a supervision order for the child to enter a specified home or residential establishment.

Although social work began in Victorian times, the

Social Work Department was created by the 1968 act and took over the social services formerly provided by local authority health and welfare systems, probation departments and children's committees. One of the provisions of the act was the appointment of social workers to provide background reports for the children's hearings and to supervise those considered to be in need of compulsory measures of care, either at home or in residential establishments.

The Children's Panel has the power to send a child to a residential assessment centre within the new system either as a place of safety or to obtain more information about the child. After 21 days, a report is sent to the panel containing an educational and psychological assessment of the child along with comments on behaviour while in the centre. The purpose of this is to enable the panel to make a decision on which form of care would serve the best interests of the child.

One of the places to which a child might be sent is a List D school. These are residential educational establishments, formerly known as approved schools, where provision is made for children aged between 8 and 16 years who are sent there by the Children's Panel as being in need of compulsory care. Children may also be placed there by the Secretary of State as the result of a court order. The schools are classified according to the age, sex and religion of the children.

An intermediate stage between voluntary social work care at home and compulsory referral to a residential centre such as a List D school is provided by the intermediate treatment centres. The term 'intermediate treatment' does not appear in the Social Work (Scotland) Act but comes from the white paper entitled 'Children in trouble' and refers to an entire range of facilities which might provide

(a) individual supervision,
(b) conventional voluntary youth organisations with special provisions for children with mild social or emotional problems,
(c) local treatment groups,
(d) intermediate treatment centres,
(e) hostel accommodation and foster care.

These facilities range from supervision at home to residential care away from home.

Between 1972 and 1980, the number of referrals

to the Reporter varied from 24,200 to 31,800 per year, the number of individual children being referred ranging from 17,000 to 22,000 per annum. These figures give no useful information about the frequency of specific reasons for referral such as delinquency, child abuse or truancy.

The police act outside this system but it is dependent on their co-operation. They can and do refer children to the Reporter for consideration of further action or they can take informal action of their own such as counselling children and parents or involving the children in local leisure activities.

In the period before 1 May 1971, solvent abusers in Lanarkshire who had come to the attention of the police were referred to the drug squad. After this date, all solvent abusers were dealt with by the newly formed Community Involvement Branch of the police which was intended to deal specifically with all aspects of crime prevention and community relations. They also had a particular interest in young people under the age of 16 who were in need of care and protection. Details of all children, including those who abused solvents, with whom the police had been involved were passed to the Community Involvement Branch using a system of contact cards. Each card contained the child's name, address, age, school, date of contact and the reason for referral along with other relevant details. The Community Involvement Branch might act on this by visiting the child's home, either at the time of the particular incident or later, or by bringing the child to the attention of other agencies such as the School Health Service, general practitioner or the Social Work Department. The police were unable, until recently, to refer children to the Reporter on the grounds of solvent abuse alone but they might do so on the grounds that the child was beyond parental control and therefore in need of help. In some districts of Glasgow from the late 1970s onwards, it became part of the standard police procedure to refer children to the Reporter if three contact cards had been completed in respect of solvent abuse because it was felt that this gave a clear indication that the child was in need of care. It was not until the Solvent Abuse (Scotland) Act 1983 came into force that solvent abuse per se became a specific ground for referral to the Reporter.

REFERENCES

1.    Martin, F.M. and Murray, K. (eds.) (1982),
The Scottish Juvenile Justice System, Scottish
Academic Press Limited, Edinburgh.
2.    Martin, F.M. and Murray, K. (eds.) (1976),
Children's Hearings, Scottish Academic Press
Limited, Edinburgh.

Appendix B

ABUSABLE AND ABUSED SOLVENTS

This table shows the chemical and trade names of solvents commonly abused by vapour inhalation, the types of domestically available products in which they are to be found and the hazard classification allocated to them in the recently introduced Classification, Packaging and Labelling of Dangerous Substances Regulations. 1984 (SI 1984. No 1244)

## Key to Hazard Classification

HF  - Highly flammable (Flashpoint less than 21°C)
F   - Flammable (Flashpoint between 21°C and 55°C)
Hi  - Harmful by inhalation
Hsk - Harmful by contact with the skin
Hsw - Harmful if swallowed
T   - Toxic

Table AB.1: Abusable Solvents and their Domestic Sources*

| Chemical name or class of compound | Trade name if relevant | Domestic products in which found | Hazards |
|---|---|---|---|
| **Aliphatic and alicyclic hydrocarbons** | | | |
| Propane, n-butane and iso-butane | | Bottled fuel gas, gas lighter fuel | HF |

Table AB.1 (Cont'd)

| Chemical name or class of compound | Trade name if relevant | Domesic products in which found | Hazards |
|---|---|---|---|
| n-hexane (generally as constituent of commercial hexane solvents | | Adhesives, shoe dyes, vehicle finishing paints, petrol | HF,Hi,Hsk |
| Other straight chain, branched chain and cyclic hydrocarbons with 6 or 8 carbon atoms | | as n-hexane | HF |
| Aromatic hydrocarbons | | | |
| Toluene | | Adhesives, shoe dyes and lacquers, vehicle finishing paints and thinners | HF,Hi |
| Xylene | | Adhesives, vehicle finishing paints and thinners | F,Hi |
| Alcohols | | | |
| Iso-propanol | | Some anti-freeze and de-icing preparations | |
| Esters | | | |
| Ethylacetate, iso-propyl acetate | | Adhesives, nail varnish and nail varnish remover | HF |

Table AB.1 (Cont'd)

| Chemical name or class of compound | Trade name if relevant | Domestic products in which found | Hazards |
|---|---|---|---|
| **Ketones** | | | |
| Acetone | | Adhesives, nail varnish and nail varnish remover | HF |
| Methyl ethyl ketone | | Adhesives | HF |
| **Chlorinated aliphatic hydrocarbons** | | | |
| Methylene chloride (dichloromethane) | | Adhesives, shoe dyes, and lacquers | Hi |
| 1,1,1-trichloroethane | Genklene | Adhesives, shoe dyes and lacquers, dry cleaning machine fluid, typescript correcting and thinners | Hi,Hsw |
| Trichloroethane | Triklone | Degreasing solvent | Hi,Hsw |
| Tetrachloroethylene | Perchloroethylene | Dry-cleaning fluid and spot remover | Hi,Hsk |
| Carbon tetrachloride | | Spot remover (rarely met) | T |

Table AB.1 (Cont'd)

| Chemical name or class of compound | Trade name if relevant | Domestic products in which found | Hazards |
|---|---|---|---|
| **Fluorine containing halogenated hydrocarbons** | | | |
| The range of substituted aliphatic hydrocarbons containing fluorine and sometimes chlorine and bromine | Arcton (and a number)<br><br>Halon (and a number) | Used as aerosol propellants in products such as hair sprays, deodorants analgesic sprays etc. | Not classified as dangerous by SI No. |

* Prepared by H.E. Akerman, Technical Liaison Manager, Evode Limited.

Abusable and Abused Solvents

Table AB.2: Products and Chemicals Known to have been Abused*

| Product | Chemical |
| --- | --- |
| Fuel gases | Butane, propane |
| Aerosols | Dichlorodifluoromethane<br>Trichlorofluoromethane |
| Fire extinguishers | Bromochlorodifluoromethane |
| Adhesives | Toluene<br>Xylene<br>Trichloroethylene<br>Tetrachloroethylene |
| Typewriter correcting fluids | 1,1,1-trichloroethane |
| Dry-cleaning and degreasing<br>agents | 1,1,1-trichloroethane<br>Tetrachloroethane<br>Tetrachloroethylene |
| Paint strippers | Dichloromethane |

* This table was prepared by Dr. J. Ramsey, Toxicology Unit, St. George's Hospital, London and lists chemicals whose abuse has been detected and gives the common products which contain them.

# POSTSCRIPT

From time to time problems emerge in our society which attract great interest and great concern. As time goes on this concern frequently produces demands that something should be done to deal with the problem. Very often the public turn to the Government or to Parliament looking for a remedy in legislation. When the matter is taken up the problems involved in legislation appear insurmountable and this may be due to lack of knowledge of the essential characteristics of the problem or of appropriate measures to counteract it.

This book has dealt with one such major problem that has manifested itself in a particularly important way over recent years. It was my privilege to meet Dr Watson as a professional witness when I was Lord Advocate. I was immediately impressed with her wide knowledge and close experience of many aspects of the problem with which this book deals and with areas of knowledge which cover the subject matter of this work.

In my opinion we are indebted to Dr Watson not only for a very thorough and illuminating study of the problem of solvent abuse, but also because I think she has shown the way in which similar problems should be tackled. Dr Watson has shown, I think, that there is no substitute for painstaking and accurate study of the facts and patterns that exist in a problem of this sort. She was well equipped by her training and experience not only to participate in the fact-finding itself but also to gather, in a comprehensive and comprehensible manner, the work of others who had studied examples of the practice of solvent abuse in the area of Strathclyde to which she devoted her principal attention and also to appreciate the bearing on the problem of Strathclyde of information available

Postscript

more generally. One of the results I think is to show very plainly that the practice of solvent abuse among children and young people in Strathclyde has not been so widespread as many feared. It has also made clear that the solvents abused are those which are very accessible but still are of use in many perfectly legitimate activities which would be seriously inhibited by any attempt to control the use of these substances. This seems a solid foundation on which to base a conclusion that legislation imposing general control on such substances is likely to produce much more disadvantage than advantage.

The work has also shown that it is easy to exaggerate the danger of solvent abuse and that if professionals endeavour to restrain such abuse among young people by exaggerated accounts of the possible consequences, the probability is that those young people who have experience of abuse will readily appreciate that these accounts of possible consequences are exaggerated with adverse effects on the credibility of the advice and of the advisers. The need is for advice which accurately reflects the facts of the situation and draws on what is known about the particular problem of the individual being advised. For example when giving advice it is important to distinguish between the chronic abuser and the person who has been brought along only occasionally to abuse solvents out of curiosity.

The work has also shown, I believe, the possibility of effective action within the framework of the Scottish legal system.

Dr Watson's work has shown, I believe, that continuing activity in this area is required but perhaps more important she has given an excellent illustration of how similar problems should be tackled in the future. Hasty remedies resorted to in face of popular clamour in relation to problems such as solvent abuse may well do more harm than good. What is required, the precise methods to be used depending on the circumstances of the individual case, is patient and careful examination of the facts by a person with skill in a number of relevant disciplines who has an understanding of the relationship of the problem under consideration to the broader picture of social, medical and economic conditions under which the problem has arisen.

I consider that the public in Scotland owe Dr Watson a great debt for the work she has so

227

devotedly done at the same time as she has been
carrying other professional burdens. This debt
relates not only to the field of solvent abuse but
by her work, she has, I consider, provided a model
for use with adaptations in the study of similar
problems which presently exist or may arise in the
future.

LORD MACKAY OF CLASHFERN
House of Lords
Westminster
London

Lord Mackay is Lord of Appeal in Ordinary, formerly
Lord Advocate for Scotland and in the latter
capacity had responsibility for prosecutions in
Scotland including prosecutions arising out of
solvent abuse.

# INDEX

Index

Index